THE TWELFTH DELUXE COLLECTOR'S EDITION OF

DAN DARE
PILOT OF THE FUTURE

DARE:
THE FINAL VOLUME

HAWK BOOKS

DAN DARE
Dare: The Final Volume
FIRST EDITION

Series Designer/Compiler: Mike Higgs

ISBN: 1 899441 25 5

Published by
HAWK BOOKS
A division of
HOSTACTION LTD
SUITE 309
CANALOT STUDIOS
222 KENSAL ROAD
LONDON W10 5BN

The Final Word

It was back in 1987 when the Deluxe Collectors Edition series of 'Dan Dare' strip cartoons began. The first volume reprinted a full colour facsimile of the first 'Dan Dare' story as it originally appeared in 'Eagle' magazine between April 1950 through to September 1951.

The response to this volume was good enough to ensure that the rest of Dan's adventures in this 2-pages-per-episode format would continue and Volume 2 right through to Volume 12 (which you are now reading) is the result. Some of you will have realised that not all of the original 'Dan Dare' adventures have been reprinted, even though this is the last volume in our series. We felt that a brief explanation is in order.

The Dan Dare Deluxe Collectors Edition series Volumes 1 to 11 have reprinted all the full colour 'Dan Dare' adventures from April 1950 through to March 1962.

It was around this point in time that the decline of 'Eagle' began and the publishers started to mess with the format of the 'Dan Dare' strip. From March '62 through to the end of May '64 the stories not only became much shorter but were relegated to black and white only or even stranger combinations such as each episode containing one and a half pages of black and white artwork with a third page in colour. We do not feel that these stories suit the style of our collection and have for this reason left them out.

Dan was returned to two full pages in colour every week from June '64 to July '65. The artwork was by Keith Watson and we have reprinted these stories in this volume.

The strip then had another format change which meant it ran across the centre spread of the comic. If we reprinted these stories in this collection, the centre of the artwork would be in danger of disappearing down the binding. This period lasted from July '65 through to the end of June '66.

Dan's adventures were finally reduced to one colour page per week for the last original story which ran from July '66 to the beginning of January '67. This story is also reproduced in this volume.

'Eagle' reverted to reprinting some of Dan's earlier adventures until it folded and was merged with 'Lion' comic in 1969.

The last story in this, our final volume is 'Operation Moss' reprinted from Eagle Annual No8 and features artwork by the original Dan Dare artist, Frank Hampson.

To keep everyone informed, here is a list of the 'Dan Dare' stories left out of the 'Deluxe' series due to incompatibility of format. The title is followed by the volume and issue numbers of the original 'Eagle' comic that they appeared in.

OPERATION EARTHSAVERS
Vol.13 No.10 to Vol.13 No.23

THE EVIL ONE
Vol.13 No.24 to Vol.13 No.32

OPERATION FIREBALL
Vol.13 No.33 to Vol.13 No.42

THE WEB OF FEAR
Vol.13 No.43 to Vol.13 No.52

OPERATION DARK STAR
Vol.14 No.1 to Vol.14 No.9

OPERATION TIME TRAP
Vol.14 No.10 to Vol.14 No.38

THE WANDERING WORLD
Vol.14 No.39 to Vol.15 No.13

THE BIG CITY CAPER
Vol.15 No.14 to Vol.15 No.22

THE SINGING SCOURGE
Vol.16 No.30 to Vol.17 No.6

GIVE ME THE MOON
Vol.17 No.7 to Vol.17 No.26

Dan Dare and Co. are always popping up in either reprints or new stories and even though after eight years we have reached the end of this particular series, we bet we haven't seen the last of that famous 'Pilot of the Future'.

Thanks to all of you who have supported the series over the years - it has been much appreciated. Now, lets Blast Off for adventure one last time...

Mike Higgs
October 1995

THE DELUXE COLLECTOR'S EDITIONS OF DAN DARE, PILOT OF THE FUTURE CHECKLIST

EAGLE
and SWIFT
6 June 1964 Vol. 15 No. 23

EVERY WEDNESDAY **6d.**

FREE INSIDE!

Great new stories begin today ... BLACKBOW ... HEROS ...
CORNELIUS DIMWORTHY and the heroes of VOODOO ISLAND!

THE MORNING DRAGGED INTO AFTERNOON, AND STILL THE WEARYING ARGUMENTS WENT ON...

MAJOR SPENCE, THERE'S A VIDEO-PHONE CALL FROM A COLONEL BANGER!

AHA! WHAT'S THE BIG IDEA OF SENDING THESE FOOLS WITH ORDERS FOR ME TO PACK AND GO OFF TO VENUS?

EH?

I'M MUCH TO BUSY TO GO! YOU AND YOUR DEPARTMENT, YOU CAN ORGANIZE SOME OTHER JOHNNY FOR THAT TRIP! I'M NOT GOING!

BUT, COLONEL BANGER, I DO ASSURE YOU...

BUT THE SCREEN CUT DEAD ON SPENCE'S WORDS...

CLICK!

WHAT WAS ALL THAT ABOUT?

TROUBLE, MAJOR?

NO—JUST COLONEL BANGER SHOUTING AT ME BECAUSE HE THINKS I'M RESPONSIBLE IN SOME WAY FOR PUTTING HIM ON THE NEXT SCHEDULE FOR VENUS! I KNOW NOTHING ABOUT IT!

NO REPLY

WE WON'T BE NEEDED HERE FOR A LONG WHILE YET— WE'D BETTER PAY BANGER A VISIT!

LATER...

I'VE GOT AN UNEASY FEELING ABOUT THAT CALL. I KNOW FOR A FACT THAT BANGER'S HANDS ARE FULL WITH EARTHSIDE PROJECTS FOR AT LEAST A MONTH. LET'S CALL HIM BACK!

BY GUM—THERE'S NOTHING LIKE A WILD GOOSE CHASE TO BREAK BOREDOM! WE'LL LOOK PROPER DAFT WHEN COLONEL BANGER TELLS US HE REFUSED TO ANSWER THE VIDEO!

I KNOW, DIGBY, HE MIGHT ALSO HAVE POPPED OUT FOR A VITAMIN PILL OR TO HAVE HIS MOUSTACHE TRIMMED —BUT I DON'T THINK SO!

NO SMOKE—AT LEAST THERE WASN'T A FIRE!

DON'T YOU THINK, SIR, THAT ALL THIS FUSS...

HELICARS IN

HE'S GONE!

AND WHAT A SHAMBLES HE'S LEFT BEHIND...

I KNEW THERE WAS SOMETHING WRONG!

EAGLE
and SWIFT
13 June 1964 Vol. 15 No. 24

EVERY WEDNESDAY 6d.

Read how to tame that bully, how to improve your cricket, how to develop real strength, how to improve your schoolwork . . .

ROOF TOP BOYS CLUB

THE TRIAL HAS FINISHED FOR THE DAY — NOW THEY'RE TAKING THE MEKON BACK TO HIS PRISON CELL!

HE COULD NEVER ESCAPE FROM THAT GUARD!

DAN DARE
Pilot of the Future
in ALL TREENS MUST DIE!

The Mekon — ex-leader of the rebel Treens of Venus — was on trial for his crimes against the Universe . . .

EVERY INCH OF AIR-SPACE ALONG THE ROUTE WAS DOUBLE-GUARDED!

CHECKPOINT RED-THIRTY. GREENGAGE PASSING NOW, ALL O.K.

LATER THAT EVENING, DAN DARE WAS AT POLICE H.Q. REPORTING BANGER'S DISAPPEARANCE...

SOMETHING IS WRONG, COMMISSIONER. COLONEL BANGER AND ASSISTANT COB HAVE VANISHED WITHOUT TRACE!

THERE MAY BE A SIMPLE REASON, ESPECIALLY WITH AN IMPULSIVE MAN LIKE BANGER! IN ANY CASE, UNDER THE MISSING PERSONS ACT OF 1987, WE MUST WAIT AT LEAST 24 HOURS TO SEE IF THEY TURN UP ON THEIR OWN!

DO YOU REALIZE THAT THERE ARE OVER TWO THOUSAND TREENS LIVING AND WORKING IN LONDON, AND THAT WE HAVE TO CHECK THEM ALL, TWICE A DAY, AS LONG AS THE MEKON IS ON TRIAL — IN CASE THEY ATTEMPT RESCUE!

MOREOVER, I HAVE EVERY AVAILABLE MAN POSTED ON MEKON SECURITY!

EAGLE
and SWIFT

20 June 1964 Vol. 15 No. 25

EVERY WEDNESDAY **6d.**

INSIDE!
DARE-DEVILS OF LÉ MANS!
The story of this week's great motor race... Page 18
PLUS
Full cutaway drawing of the world's latest sports car... Page 19

THERE GOES OUR MASTER ON HIS WAY HOME TO VENUS!

SF FERRY 8

DAN DARE
Pilot of the Future
in ALL TREENS MUST DIE!

Two friends of Dan Dare – Colonel Banger and Technician Cob – had mysteriously disappeared, and the Treens intended to use them to convey the Mekon secretly to his home planet, Venus. Within an hour of the Mekon's prison break . . .

KEITH WATSON

VIDEONEWS REPORTS FLASHED AROUND THE GLOBE ...

THE PEOPLE
MEKON AT LARGE

...A WIDESPREAD SEARCH IS NOW IN OPERATION ...

LONDON WAS SCOURED!

EVERY PINNACLE WAS SCANNED, EVERY DARK CORNER PROBED ...

EVERY AVAILABLE MAN WAS SUMMONED FOR DUTY...

COLONEL DARE! AN URGENT CALL FROM THE PRIME MINISTER!

DAN DARE'S HEADQUARTERS HAD TRIED TO MAKE DIRECT CONTACT WITH THE MAGENTA...

THERE'S A SIGNAL BLOCKAGE AROUND THE MAGENTA. WE'RE STILL TRYING TO BREAK THROUGH, SIR, USING ALL FREQUENCIES!

THEN SOMETHING STRANGE IS HAPPENING—AND IT SMELLS STRONGLY OF THE MEKON!

THREE GREEN STARS—THAT'S THE INTERNATIONAL SIGNAL FOR 'I'M COMING ABOARD'!

THEN STAND BY THE MAIN AIR-LOCK! THIS VISIT MAY HAVE SOMETHING TO DO WITH THE RADIO BLACKOUT!

AYE, AYE, SIR!

EVER SINCE THE MEKON HAD FIRST BEEN DRIVEN FROM VENUS AND REPLACED BY PRESIDENT SONDAR, THE TREENS HAD LEARNED TO CO-OPERATE AND WORK WITH EARTHMEN ON FRIENDLY TERMS. THEREFORE THE PASSENGERS AND CREW ALIKE WERE THOROUGHLY UNPREPARED FOR ALL THAT HAPPENED NEXT ABOARD THE MAGENTA!

NO ONE WILL MOVE UNTIL ORDERED TO DO SO!

B-BUT... OOOH!

SILENCE!

THE TREENS ENTERED THE BAGGAGE HOLD AND BEGAN RIPPING OPEN THE SEALED CONTAINERS!

HEY, CAREFUL—THAT'S MY...

SIT DOWN!

OOOH! MY HEAD!

THE TREENS FOUND A TRUNK BELONGING TO COLONEL BANGER, AND PULLED IT OPEN...

JUST LOOK AT THAT!

WHAT IS IT?

THE MEKON!

BUT ONE PASSENGER SEEMED UNCONCERNED BY THE ARCH-TREEN'S APPEARANCE. HE WAS COLONEL BANGER, WHOSE EYES WERE BLEARY AND WHOSE HEAD ACHED LIKE A MARBLE SQUEEZED IN A STEAM-VICE!

OW-OH! UH! WHERE AM I? I FEEL AS THOUGH I'VE BEEN DRUGGED!

K.W.

COB! THOSE TREENS? WHAT ARE THEY DOING? AND THE MEKON—HE SHOULDN'T BE HERE!

DON'T WORRY, SIR! THE TREENS SAID EVERYTHING WOULD BE ALL RIGHT WHEN THEY ASKED US TO HELP THEM!

US HELP RESCUE THE MEKON—THEN I MUST HAVE BEEN DRUGGED! AND COB'S STILL UNDER, SO IT SEEMS!

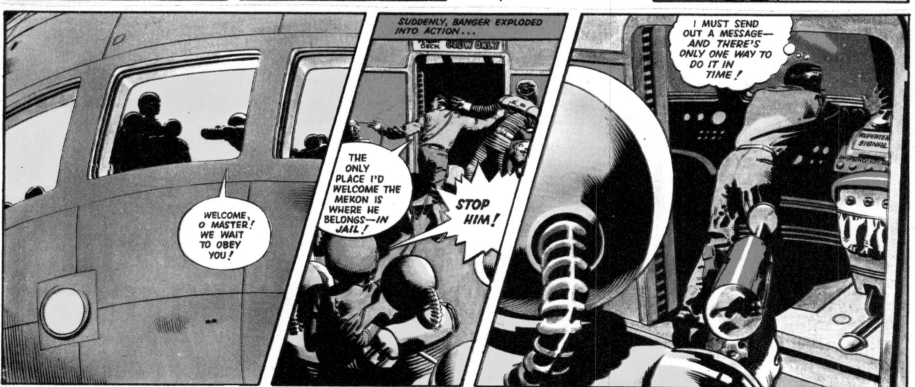

WELCOME, O MASTER! WE WAIT TO OBEY YOU!

SUDDENLY, BANGER EXPLODED INTO ACTION...

THE ONLY PLACE I'D WELCOME THE MEKON IS WHERE HE BELONGS—IN JAIL!

STOP HIM!

I MUST SEND OUT A MESSAGE—AND THERE'S ONLY ONE WAY TO DO IT IN TIME!

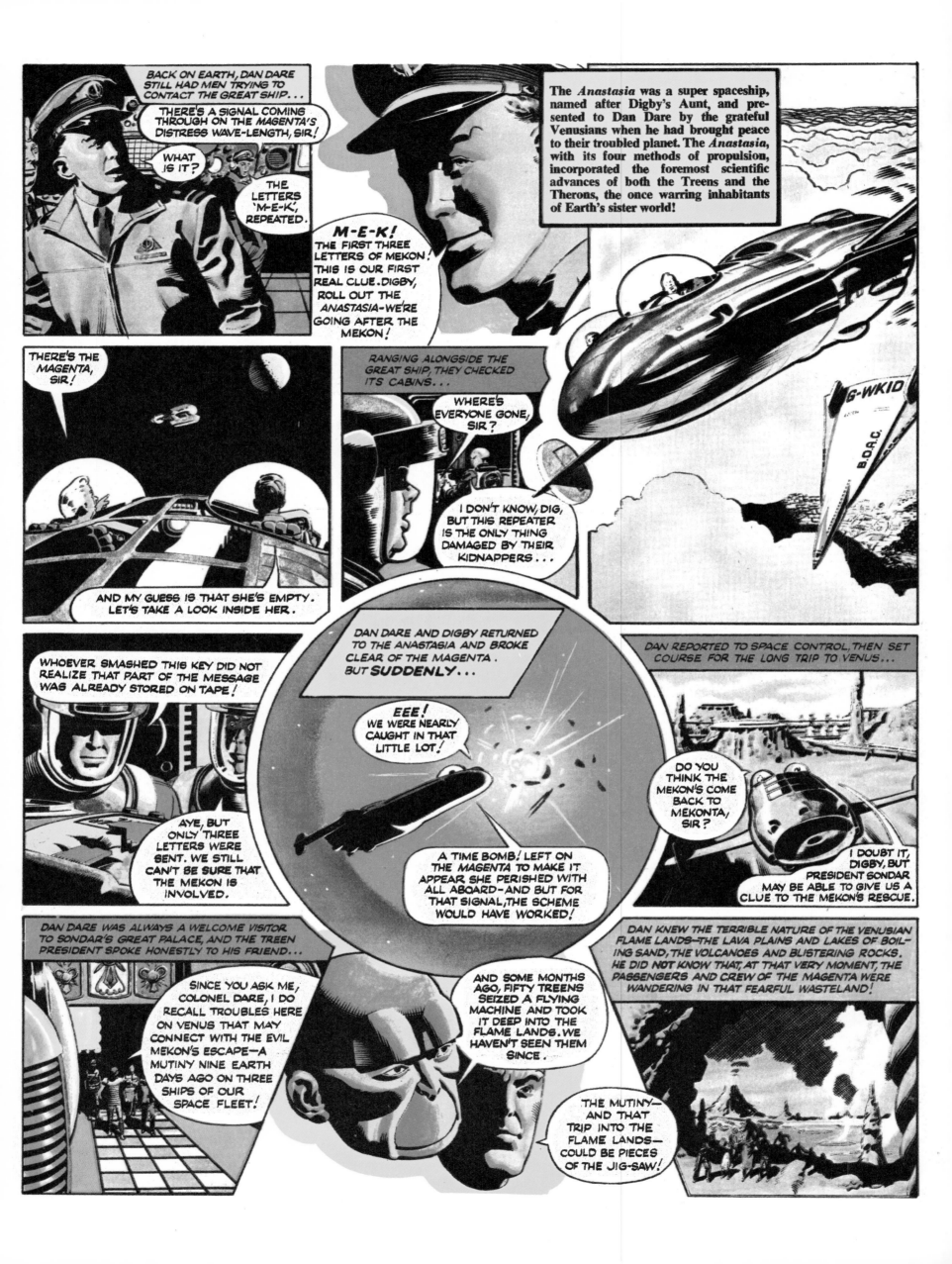

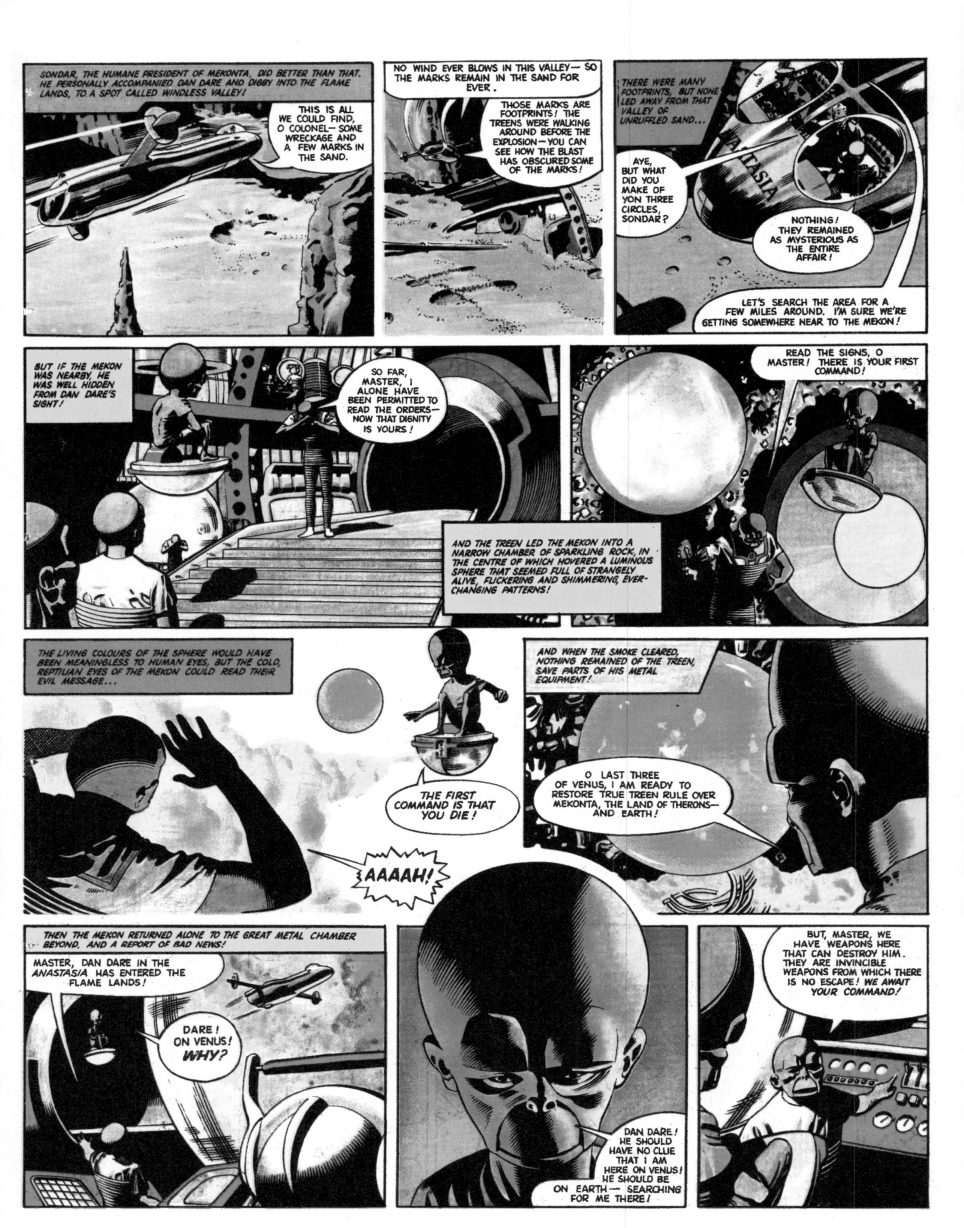

THE RESCUED MAGENTA PASSENGERS WERE RUSHED TO THE TREEN CITY, WHERE FOOD AND MEDICAL ATTENTION WERE SPEEDILY PROVIDED...

THE MEKON IS DEFINITELY HERE ON VENUS, DAN! YOU CAN BE SURE OF THAT—WE BROUGHT HIM HERE!

AND HE'S WELL SET UP! TONS OF GEAR—AND THE TREENS TO MANAGE IT!

AT LEAST WE TOLD THEM NOTHING ABOUT THE PROJECT WE WERE ENGAGED ON—IMPROVING THE NEURO-TREMBLER MOB-DISPERSAL GUN!

AND THE DRUGS HE USED TO MAKE US SMUGGLE HIM OFF EARTH IN OUR LUGGAGE, THEY'RE NEW STUFF! WE KNEW WHAT WE WERE DOING, BUT WE COULDN'T STOP OURSELVES!

WHILE DAN'S FRIENDS RESTED, HIS ARCH-ENEMY WAS MOVING INTO ACTION!

SEND OUT THE SIGNAL FOR THE MOBS TO ASSEMBLE!

BUT MASTER, IT IS RUMOURED THAT SONDAR AND THE SPACE FLEET ARE IN POSSESSION OF A SECRET GUN THAT CAN DISPERSE A MOB WITH A SINGLE SHOT!

WE KNOW THE SECRET OF THE NEURO-TREMBLER! WE EXTRACTED IT FROM BANGER UNDER DEEP SEDATION. HE WON'T REMEMBER TELLING US. HE EVEN DESCRIBED IMPROVEMENTS HE WAS ABOUT TO INVENT!

AND ONCE AGAIN, THE MEKON RETREATED TO AN EERIE CAVE AND THE WEIRD SUSPENDED GLOBE...

O LAST THREE OF VENUS—ALL PREPARATIONS ARE PERFECT!

WHAT WAS TO BECOME KNOWN AS THE GREAT SIEGE OF MEKONTA BEGAN QUIETLY...

LOOK COLONEL DARE, SIGNS LIKE THAT HAVE SUDDENLY APPEARED ABOUT MEKONTA!

THEN...

O PRESIDENT, HUNDREDS OF THESE DISCS HAVE BEEN FOUND FLOATING AMONG THE ISLANDS!

EE, NOT TO WORRY, LAD. IT MAY BE RAG WEEK AT LOCAL UNIVERSITY!

WE SHOULD BE WORRIED, DIGBY—DON'T YOU RECOGNIZE THE SIGN OF THE MEKON!

DAN DARE KNEW THAT THE MEKON WAS ABOUT TO MAKE HIS FIRST MOVE, BUT WHEN—WHERE—HOW? THESE TENSION-LADEN QUESTIONS WERE SOON TO BE ANSWERED...

PRESIDENT SONDAR, MANY TREENS ARE LEAVING THEIR WORK AND RUNNING TOWARDS THE LAKE—THEY NO LONGER OBEY ORDERS! *THE TREENS ARE IN REVOLT!*

SOON, A LIVID RED GLOW RADIATED FROM THE OBJECT IN THE LAKE. TREENS FROM THE CITY RAN BLINDLY TOWARDS IT...

STOP THEM, SONDAR—THEY'RE COMMITTING MASS SUICIDE!

I CANNOT STOP THEM, FOR THEY OBEY THE COMMANDS OF A MASTER MORE POWERFUL THAN I!

THE RED GLOW TURNED INTO A GRUESOME BLUE...

THERE IS SOMETHING YOU CAN DO, SONDAR! GO AND GET YOUR NEURO-TREMBLER ANTI-MOB GUN. USE IT NOW!

IT IS IN THE ARMOURY — I SHALL SEND FOR IT!

THE PALACE ORGANISATION WAS ULTRA-EFFICIENT. ELECTRONIC SIGNALS AND VACUUM SHAFTS BROUGHT THE WEAPON ON TO THE ROOF WITHIN SECONDS...

IT'S ONE OF THE EARLY MODELS...

IT SHOULD BE EFFICIENT ENOUGH, THOUGH!

DAN TOOK CAREFUL AIM AT THE CENTRE OF ONE MOB...

...AND VIBRANT NERVE SIGNALS WERE FIRED TO SOOTHE THE OVER-EXCITED BRAINS OF FRENZIED TREENS...

STRAINED OF THEIR JANGLING FEVER, A SECTION OF THE TREENS TURNED AWAY, ALL MEMORY OF THEIR DEATH-CHARGE OBLITERATED...

THEN...

INSIDE THE DOME OF DEATH IN THE LAKE, A REPORT WAS MADE TO THAT MASTER-MIND OF EVIL — WHO HAD JUST WATCHED THE DEATH OF A THOUSAND TREENS...

SOME TURN ASIDE! THE NEURO-TREMBLER GUN HAS BEEN USED!

THEN WE SHALL NEUTRALIZE IT!

DAN AIMED AT A SECOND SECTION OF THE DOOMED TREENS —AND PULLED THE TRIGGER THAT WOULD SAVE THEM...

AAAAH!

EAGLE
and SWIFT
8 August 1964 Vol. 15 No. 32
EVERY WEDNESDAY 6d.

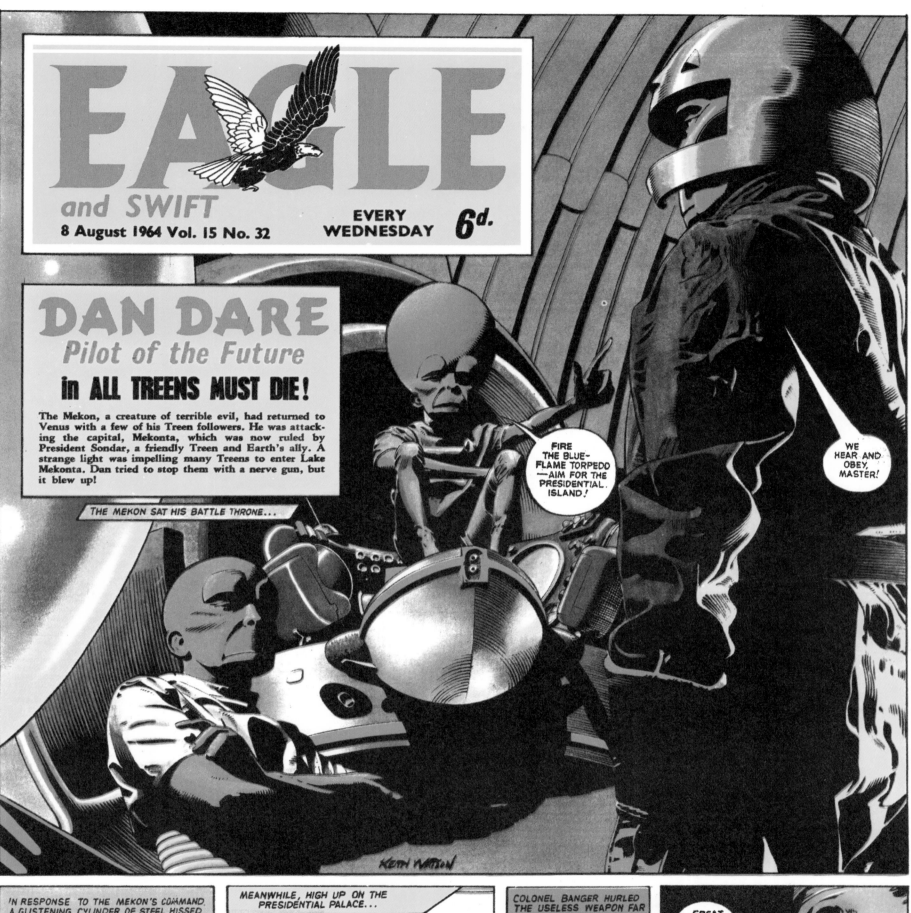

DAN DARE
Pilot of the Future
in ALL TREENS MUST DIE!

The Mekon, a creature of terrible evil, had returned to Venus with a few of his Treen followers. He was attacking the capital, Mekonta, which was now ruled by President Sondar, a friendly Treen and Earth's ally. A strange light was impelling many Treens to enter Lake Mekonta. Dan tried to stop them with a nerve gun, but it blew up!

THE MEKON SAT HIS BATTLE THRONE...

FIRE THE BLUE-FLAME TORPEDO —AIM FOR THE PRESIDENTIAL ISLAND!

WE HEAR AND OBEY, MASTER!

IN RESPONSE TO THE MEKON'S COMMAND, A GLISTENING CYLINDER OF STEEL HISSED THROUGH THE TEPID WATERS OF LAKE MEKONTA...

MEANWHILE, HIGH UP ON THE PRESIDENTIAL PALACE...

ARE YOU HURT, SIR?

I'LL DEAL WITH IT!

EYEBROWS SINGED, NOTHING WORSE! BUT THAT NEURO GUN'S BURNING LIKE A FIRE-BOMB!

COLONEL BANGER HURLED THE USELESS WEAPON FAR OUT INTO THE LAKE...

GREAT SCOTT! WHAT WAS THAT?

THE GUN HIT SOMETHING!

IT WAS A TORPEDO, AIMED AT THIS ISLAND!

AND IF IT WAS ONE OF THE MEKON'S FIENDISH DEVICES, IT'S AS WELL FOR US THAT I DID KNOCK IT OFF COURSE!

THEY WATCHED THE SINISTER MISSILE UNTIL IT HIT A NEARBY ISLAND, SPLATTERING IT WITH A COLD, BLUE FIRE!

MEANWHILE, THE MEKON'S CITADEL STILL SWATHED THE CITY BUILDINGS AND THE WHOLE POPULATION WITH EERIE, COLOURED LIGHT—A LIGHT THAT SEEMED TO PENETRATE THE MINDS OF TREENS, IMPELLING THEM BY THE HUNDRED TO SWARM BLINDLY TOWARDS THE LAKE WATERS...

COME ON, DIGBY—TO THE ANASTASIA! OUR FIRST TASK IS TO MASK THAT LIGHT!

RIGHT, DIGBY—LET'S MAKE SMOKE!

AND DAN FOLDED DOWN LAYER UPON LAYER OF COILING SMOKE UPON THE WATERS UNTIL THE SPIKE OF DEADLY LIGHT WAS COMPLETELY SMOTHERED!

THE CITY TREENS SLOWED THEIR IMPULSIVE STAMPEDE TO WATERY SUICIDE!

DAN LANDED THE ANASTASIA NEAR THE PRESIDENTIAL PALACE...

THE SITUATION IS A LOT CALMER NOW, SONDAR! YOU'VE A FEW MINUTES BEFORE THE SMOKE CLEARS TO USE YOUR PALACE GUARDS TO RESTORE COMPLETE CONTROL!

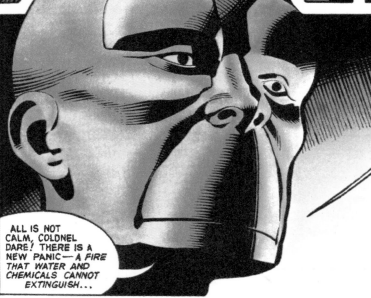

ALL IS NOT CALM, COLONEL DARE! THERE IS A NEW PANIC—A FIRE THAT WATER AND CHEMICALS CANNOT EXTINGUISH...

THE BLUE FIRE TORPEDO HAS ALMOST ENVELOPED THAT ISLAND! SOON IT WILL SPREAD THROUGHOUT ALL MEKONTA...

WE ARE ALL DOOMED!

THE ALARM WAS RAISED!

THE MEKON'S SOLDIERS ARE IN THE CITY!

THE SINISTER INVADERS SURROUNDED THE NEAREST LARGE BUILDING, KILLING ALL WHO STOOD IN THEIR WAY!

WITHIN A MINUTE, THE GREAT STRUCTURE WAS BOILING SMOKE LIKE A CLAY POT ON A FIRE!

CHOKING TREENS TUMBLED FROM THE SMOKING BUILDING AND STAGGERED BLINDLY BEFORE THE GUNS OF THE MEKON'S SOLDIERS...

THE SITUATION'S TAKEN A TURN FOR THE WORSE! BANGER, CAN YOU HELP SONDAR HERE WITH DEFENCE?

SURE, DAN, BUT WHERE ARE YOU GOING?

I'M GOING TO FIND 'THE LAST THREE OF VENUS'! IT'S A GAMBLE, BUT IF THEY EXIST AND I CAN FIND THEM, IT MAY CAUSE THE MEKON TO BREAK OFF THE SIEGE AND COME TO THEIR AID!

COME ON, COB— SHOW ME WHERE THE MEKON RELEASED YOU IN THE FLAME LANDS. WHEN WE'VE FOUND THE PLACE, DIGBY CAN FLY ON TO THE SOUTH AND BRING IN REINFORCEMENTS!

BY GUM, THE WHOLE POPULATION'S GOING OVER TO THE MEKON— LOOK DOWN THERE!

IT SEEMS TO ME AS THOUGH THEY WERE PREPARED FOR THIS SIEGE— THEY'RE A READY-MADE FIFTH COLUMN!

COME ON, LADS! WE'VE TIME TO SHAKE UP THAT MOB BEFORE WE LEAVE FOR THE FLAME LANDS!

ANASTASIA

DAN DARE TOOK THE GLEAMING ANASTASIA IN A THUNDERING POWER DIVE FROM THE PALACE ROOF. THE MOB BELOW TURNED— AND AT LEAST ONE WEAPON WAS RAISED IN AIM!

IMMEDIATELY, A SECOND BATCH OF SINISTER TORPEDOES LEFT THE MEKON'S GRIM STRONGHOLD...

THE OCCUPANTS OF THE METAL MISSILES BURST FROM THE MURKY GREEN WATERS LIKE DEMONS OF THE DEEP...

AT THE SAME TIME, THE TREEN INHABITANTS OF ONE ISLAND WERE SWARMING ACROSS A HIGH BRIDGE...

THE MEKON! THE MEKON! WE COME TO JOIN THE MEKON!

WITHIN SECONDS, THE MEKON'S CALLOUS ORDER WAS RUTHLESSLY OBEYED!

ALL TREENS MUST DIE!

EEEEEH!

COLONEL BANGER AND PRESIDENT SONDAR WATCHED HELPLESSLY FROM THE PRESIDENTIAL PALACE...

THE SLAUGHTER'S TERRIBLE, SONDAR! WHY ARE THE MEKON'S STRONG-ARM MOB ATTACKING THOSE WHO WANT TO JOIN THEM?

THEY WILL BE OBEYING THE MEKON'S ORDER — BUT EVEN I CANNOT UNDERSTAND WHY THE MEKON SHOULD ISSUE SUCH A COMMAND!

DAN DARE SAW NOTHING OF THE TERRIBLE SCENE IN MEKONTA. HE HAD FLOWN DEEP INTO THE DREADED FLAME LANDS, SEARCHING FOR THE 'LAST THREE OF VENUS', NOT KNOWING WHO OR WHAT THEY WERE!

THIS IS THE APPROXIMATE AREA WHERE YOU WERE RELEASED BY THE MEKON, COB?

YES, BUT I PLOTTED THE SOURCE OF THE RADIO BEAM I DETECTED IN MEKONTA RATHER MORE TO THE RIGHT OF HERE.

THE CLUES WERE AS SLENDER AS MICRO-THREADS, BUT THEY WERE ALL THAT DAN POSSESSED IN HIS SEARCH FOR 'THE LAST THREE'...

BY GUM, WE'RE ON THE TRAIL! THERE'S A WHOLE CLUSTER OF TREEN-TYPE LANDING MARKS IN THE SAND IN YON VALLEY!

WE'VE SEEN THESE MARKS BEFORE! WE'RE SURE THEY ARE MADE BY SOME KIND OF AIRCRAFT!

SEEMS A POINTLESS PLACE TO LAND — THERE'S NOTHING HERE BUT SAND AND ROCK!

LOOK OUT — AN AVALANCHE!

BUT THE 'ROCK FALL' WAS MACHINE-CONTROLLED TO REVEAL A GREAT HOLLOW IN THE CLIFF, FROM THE INCREDIBLE DARKNESS OF WHICH THRUST A SHIMMERING PURPLE LIGHT!

WHAT IS IT? WHAT IS THAT THING?

KEEP BACK! KEEP OUT OF ITS WAY!

EAGLE
and SWIFT
12 September 1964 Vol. 15 No. 37 — EVERY WEDNESDAY — 6d.

DAN DARE
Pilot of the Future
in ALL TREENS MUST DIE!

The evil Mekon had escaped justice and was besieging the Treen capital of Mekonta. Dan Dare believed that the Mekon was not the only leader of the revolt against the friendly President Sondar, and was setting out to find the Mekon's legendary allies, the 'Last Three of Venus'. In a scorched valley in the Flame Lands . .

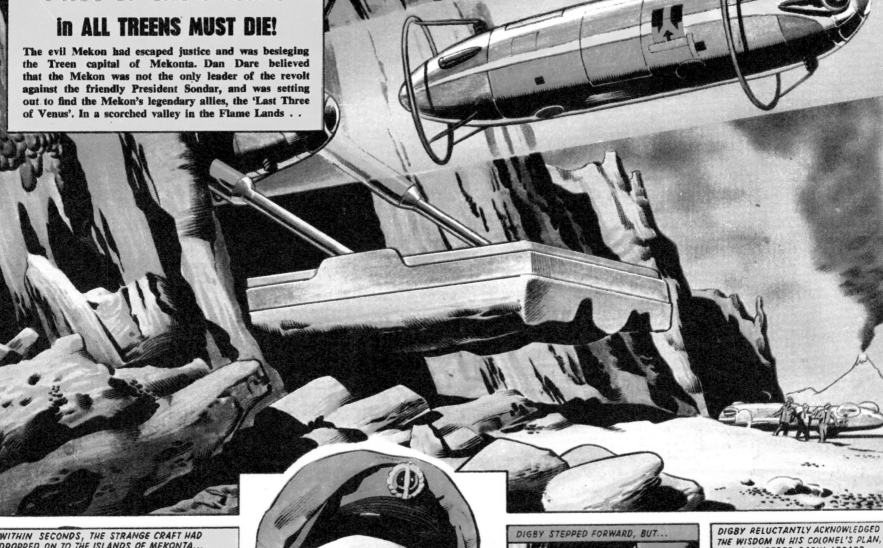

WITHIN SECONDS, THE STRANGE CRAFT HAD DROPPED ON TO THE ISLANDS OF MEKONTA...

...REINFORCEMENTS HAD ARRIVED TO AID THE MEKON!

SO THIS IS WHERE THE MEKON'S HELP COMES FROM — LET'S SEE WHO SENDS IT!

DIGBY STEPPED FORWARD, BUT...

SORRY, DIG. THE THERONS IN THE SOUTH KNOW YOU, SO I WANT YOU TO PERSUADE THEM TO SEND HELP TO SONDAR. HE'LL BE RELYING ON THAT HELP IF COB AND I FIND NOTHING IN THIS CAVE!

DIGBY RELUCTANTLY ACKNOWLEDGED THE WISDOM IN HIS COLONEL'S PLAN, AND CLAMBERED SADLY ABOARD THE ANASTASIA—KNOWING IT MORE THAN POSSIBLE THAT HE WOULD NEVER SEE HIS TWO GOOD FRIENDS AGAIN!

GOOD LUCK, COLONEL DARE! YOU'LL NEED IT, IF ANYONE DOES!

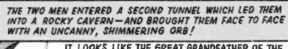

DAN DARE WAS TRAPPED! A STRANGE ROBOT MACHINE WAS LURCHING UNSTEADILY ALONG THE PASSAGE. QUIVERING METAL ARMS PROBED TOWARDS HIM...

A ROBOT SHACKLE SNAPPED AROUND DAN DARE'S ARM!

THE MACHINE DRAGGED ITS HUMAN PRISONER AWAY...

PRAY THAT COB HAD BETTER LUCK THAN I!

WHILE MACHINES HELD DAN DARE, FIRE HUNTED TECHNICIAN COB!

IT'S HOPELESS ME TRYING TO GET BACK THROUGH THAT FIRE AND HELP THE COLONEL, BUT THERE'S PLENTY FOR ME TO DO OUT HERE!

AND HE SLIPPED A SLIM TOOL FROM HIS POCKET AND TURNED TOWARDS THE BANK OF TREEN MACHINERY THAT SO FASCINATED HIS MECHANICAL MIND!

MEANWHILE, DAN DARE WAS EXPERIENCING ONE OF THE STRANGEST JOURNEYS OF HIS LIFE, PAST FURNACES THAT GLOWED WITH EVERY HUE OF MOLTEN METAL...

IT'S LIKE SOME FANTASTIC METAL FOUNDRY!

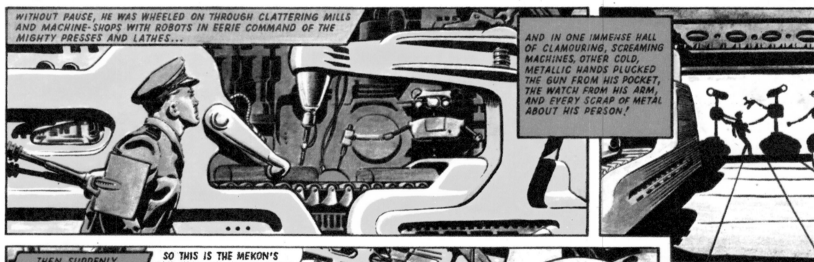

WITHOUT PAUSE, HE WAS WHEELED ON THROUGH CLATTERING MILLS AND MACHINE-SHOPS WITH ROBOTS IN EERIE COMMAND OF THE MIGHTY PRESSES AND LATHES...

AND IN ONE IMMENSE HALL OF CLAMOURING, SCREAMING MACHINES, OTHER COLD, METALLIC HANDS PLUCKED THE GUN FROM HIS POCKET, THE WATCH FROM HIS ARM, AND EVERY SCRAP OF METAL ABOUT HIS PERSON!

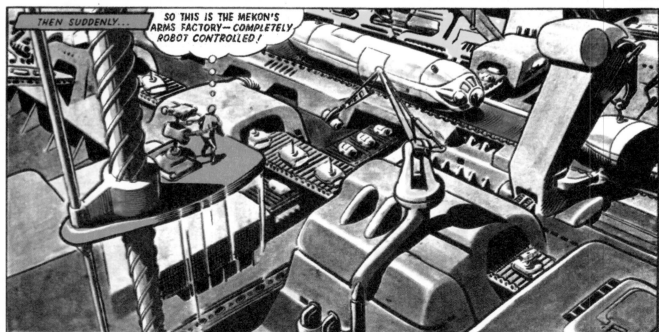

THEN SUDDENLY...

SO THIS IS THE MEKON'S ARMS FACTORY—COMPLETELY ROBOT CONTROLLED!

THE LIFT STOPPED—AND A GREAT GLASSY EYE PEERED UNBLINKINGLY AT HIS FACE!

EAGLE

26 September 1964 Vol. 15 No. 39 — EVERY WEDNESDAY — 6d.

CORNY GOES SLEEPWALKING — PAGE 3

HEROS Defies the MONSTER in the LAKE! — PAGE 10

THE STORY OF THE OLYMPIC GAMES — PAGE 16

FASTER - FASTER! History of the World's Land-Speed Record — PAGE 18

DAN DARE
Pilot of the Future
in ALL TREENS MUST DIE!

The evil Mekon was besieging Mekonta and, in order to draw off his attack, Dan Dare had attempted to penetrate the secret place of the Last Three of Venus, the Mekon's masters. However, Dan was captured by robot machinery in a vast factory area, and lifted high into the air . . .

IDENTIFY YOURSELF AND STATE YOUR PURPOSE!

I AM COLONEL DAN DARE — MY PURPOSE IS TO CAPTURE THE MEKON!

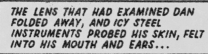

THE LENS THAT HAD EXAMINED DAN FOLDED AWAY, AND ICY STEEL INSTRUMENTS PROBED HIS SKIN, FELT INTO HIS MOUTH AND EARS...

WHO ARE YOU? WHAT ARE YOU DOING?

I AM ONE OF THE LAST THREE!

I INVENT ALL THAT IS REQUIRED FOR PEACE AND WAR!

EVEN AS IT SPOKE, THE TREEN CREATURE'S STRANGE METAL LIMBS NEVER CEASED RUNNING BACK AND FORTH ACROSS THE PANELS OF LIGHTS, STROKING AND PRODDING THEM TO EVOKE NEW AND CHANGING COLOUR PATTERNS.

DAN REALIZED THAT THIS WAS HOW THE SUPER TREEN COMMANDED HIS ARMY OF ROBOT MACHINES. THEN, SUDDENLY, IT SPOKE INTO THE HOT, EMPTY AIR...

THIS ANIMAL POSSESSES NOTHING OF MECHANICAL IMPORTANCE!/ I SHALL PASS HIM ON FOR PSYCHOLOGICAL AND NEURO-REACTION TESTS!

NOW WHO IS HE TALKING TO?

SUDDENLY, DAN WAS FLUNG THROUGH THE AIR!

DAN DARE CARTWHEELED HELPLESSLY INTO A FUNNEL OF SWIRLING VAPOUR...

THE STRANDS OF THE 'RAINBOW MIST' TUGGED AT HIS LIMBS, RESTRAINING THEM AS THEY FLAILED VIOLENTLY BACK AND FORTH!

THE STUFF FILLED HIS EYES AND THE ODOUR FROM IT SWIRLED INTO HIS BRAIN AND STRANGE PATTERNS WHIRLED AROUND HIM...

THEN, IN A DREAM-LIKE WAY, HE FELT STRANGE SENSATIONS FROM BOYHOOD DAYS...

...HE SAW HIS SMILING FRIENDS OF LATER YEARS— HIS LEERING ENEMIES, TOO...

AND WHEN HIS STORE OF MEMORIES WAS FINISHED— HE WAS TOSSED ASIDE LIKE A 'SECOND-HAND BOOK!'

IT WAS AS THOUGH HE HAD BEEN MADE TO RELIVE HIS WHOLE LIFE IN ONE INSTANT OF TIME!

MY MIND HAS BEEN READ! SOMEONE OR SOMETHING HAS EXAMINED EVERY MEMORY, THOUGHT AND AMBITION I EVER HAD!

WHAT IS THIS PLACE?

DAN DARE, YOU ARE LIVING THE LAST HOUR OF YOUR LIFE!

GREAT SCOTT!

EAGLE

3 October 1964 Vol. 15 No. 40 — EVERY WEDNESDAY — 6d.

DAN DARE
Pilot of the Future
in ALL TREENS MUST DIE!

Dan Dare believed that the Mekon's attack on Mekonta was inspired by the mysterious *Last Three of Venus*. One by one, he sought them out in the Flame Lands of Venus, hoping to divert the Mekon's forces, but they wouldn't listen . . .

YOU ARE THE ONE WHO HAS CAUSED THE MEKON'S PAST FAILURES — THEREFORE YOUR EXISTENCE MUST NOW BE ENDED!

THE EVIL MEKON WAS BESIEGING THE VENUSIAN CITY OF MEKONTA FROM A HUGE METAL FORTRESS SUBMERGED BENEATH THE LAKE

ALL HULL DAMAGE HAS BEEN REPAIRED, O MASTER!

THEN WE SHALL RISE TO THE SURFACE — AT ONCE!

PARTIES OF THE MEKON'S ARMED TREENS WERE ALREADY IN THE CITY, HORDES OF INHABITANTS GROVELLED IN SURRENDER...

BUT THE MEKON'S TROOPS ARE STILL FIRING — THEY'RE SHOWING NO MERCY!

THE MEKON HAD GIVEN AN ORDER!

ALL TREENS MUST DIE! TAKE NO PRISONERS!

MEANWHILE, IN THE STRONGHOLD OF THE LAST THREE...

YOU MUST DIE, DAN DARE!

AND ALL TREENS MUST DIE. THE PRESENT RACE HAS FAILED REPEATEDLY TO GAIN SUPREME INTERPLANETARY POWER, SO AT THE MEKON'S COMMAND WE HAVE DEVISED A NEW TREEN. MILLIONS WILL BE EVOLVED TO REPLACE THE FAULTY TREENS EVEN NOW BEING EXTERMINATED!

VAINLY, DAN TRIED TO STRIKE OUT AT THE EVIL CREATURE FLOATING BEFORE HIM...

YOUR PUNY EFFORTS WILL GAIN YOU NOTHING, EARTHMAN, AND NOTHING IN THE UNIVERSE WILL STOP THE NEW TREENS BRINGING VENUS, EARTH AND ALL THE PLANETS OF THE SOLAR SYSTEM UNDER SCIENTIFIC TREEN CONTROL!

BACK IN MEKONTA, THE HEAVILY-ARMED MEKON TREENS DESCENDED UPON SONDAR'S PALACE...

HERE THEY COME, SONDAR! AT LEAST WE'LL GO DOWN FIGHTING!

IN HIS FLOATING CITADEL, THE MEKON WATCHED THE GALLANT FIGHT OF COLONEL BANGER AND PRESIDENT SONDAR, AND WHEN THEY WERE FINALLY OVERPOWERED...

WE SHALL SPARE YOUR LIVES IF YOU TELL US WHERE DAN DARE IS HIDING!

HE'S HIDING NOWHERE! HE'S GONE TO SORT OUT THE LAST THREE OF VENUS!

IN AN URGENCY AKIN TO PANIC, THE MEKON TURNED TO HIS STRANGE LINK WITH THE WEIRD LAST THREE OF VENUS!

THE EARTH LETTER 'D'! 'D' FOR DARE— SO HE HAS FOUND THE LAST THREE!

THE MEKON KNEW OF THE COURAGE OF DAN DARE. HE HAD EXPERIENCED HIS GRIM DETERMINATION NEVER TO BE BEATEN—AND HE FEARED FOR THE LAST THREE WHEN FACED BY HIS GREATEST ENEMY! SO...

RELEASE THE PRISONERS! WE MUST RETURN TO THE CITADEL AT ONCE—BY ORDER OF THE MEKON!

TO THE TREENS, THE MEKON'S WORD WAS A COMMAND, AND DISOBEDIENCE, NO MATTER WHAT THE EXCUSE, MEANT DEATH!

WE WERE SAVED BY THE BELL, EH, SONDAR?

MINUTES LATER, THE TERRIBLE STRONGHOLD OF THE MEKON ROSE FROM THE COLOURED WATERS OF LAKE MEKONTA AND BORE THE EVIL GREEN GENIUS AND HIS RUTHLESS ARMY TOWARDS THE FLAME LANDS...

BUT THE MAN THE MEKON HASTENED TO DESTROY WAS PLUMMETING TO AN UNKNOWN FATE...

AAAH! I'M FALLING!

DAN FELL FOR WHAT SEEMED AN ETERNITY THROUGH THE MIST OF SEETHING FIRE, UNTIL IT SPEWED HIM ON TO A SLAB OF ICY, VILE-SMELLING ROCK...

WHAT PLACE IS THIS?

THIS IS THE PLACE CALLED LIFE—THE PLACE OF YOUR EXTERMINATION AND DEATH!

A DOZEN RED HANDS GRIPPED DAN DARE'S LIMBS WITH SUCH FORCE THAT THEY BRUISED HIS FLESH! HE RESISTED, BUT WAS LIFTED AS THOUGH HE WERE A MERE CHILD!

OUR WORK IS COMPLETE! SEE THE HARVEST OF MY TOIL, FOR I HAVE CREATED NEW TREENS— A WHOLE RACE OF PERFECT TREENS...

TREENS THAT WILL OBEY THE MEKON WITHOUT FAULT! HERE IS THE ARMY THAT WILL AWAKEN AND WIN VENUS, THE EARTH, AND ALL THE PLANETS—IN THE NAME OF THE MEKON!

THEN WHY AREN'T THEY AWAKE AND FIGHTING NOW?

NOT ONE PERFECT TREEN WILL LEAVE HERE UNTIL THE LAST OF THE OLD RACE HAS BEEN WIPED OUT! THERE MUST BE NO RISK THAT THEY'LL BECOME INFECTED WITH SONDAR'S DISEASE OF KINDNESS AND FRIENDSHIP TOWARDS EARTHMEN! THEREFORE, ALL TREENS MUST DIE!

ALTHOUGH THE MINIONS OF THE LAST THREE HELD DAN DARE HELPLESS, THE MYSTERIOUS 'D' DISTRESS SIGNAL CONTINUED — FIRING THE MEKON INTO PANIC-ACTION AS HE SPED ACROSS THE FLAME LANDS IN HIS CITADEL!

EMERGENCY SPEED! USE ALL AVAILABLE POWER—WITH DAN DARE IN THE HALLS OF THE LAST THREE, ANY SECOND COULD SPELL DISASTER TO MY PLANS!

LIKE A THUNDERCLAP, NEWS OF THE EVIL TYRANT'S HOME-COMING BURST THROUGH THE MYSTERIOUS CAVERNS WHERE DAN WAS HELD!

THE MEKON HAS RETURNED!

IN THE INSTANT THAT HIS TORTURERS' CONCENTRATION WAS DIVERTED, DAN ACTED!

SO YOU WANT TO KNOW ABOUT COURAGE, EH? WELL, THIS IS IT—I'D SOONER DIE FIGHTING THAN AS A SPECIMEN ON A SLAB!

EEEK!

YOUR DISPLAY OF COURAGE WILL BE BRIEF, DAN DARE!

IN THEIR EFFORTS TO HANG ON TO THEIR PRISONER, THE TWO REMAINING RED TREENS WERE PULLED INTO THE FIERY DEATH INTENDED FOR DAN...

NOW IT'S YOUR TURN FOR SOME PUNISHMENT!

THE SUPER TREEN DODGED AND SCREECHED IN VAIN!

BUT HE WASN'T FINISHED YET...

EAGLE
AND Boys' World
17 October 1964 Vol. 15 No. 42 · EVERY WEDNESDAY · 6d.

INSIDE FREE! OLYMPIC SPECIAL PRESENTED WITH and Boys' World

DAN DARE
Pilot of the Future
in ALL TREENS MUST DIE!

The Treens of Venus were being wiped out by their masters – who had created a more perfect race to replace them and conquer Venus and Earth. Dan Dare was grappling with one of the masters (called The Last Three of Venus) in an underground cavern, but the powerful Mekon had been recalled to the sinister caverns, and he vowed death to Dan Dare!

WE WERE RECALLED BECAUSE DAN DARE IS IN THESE CAVERNS! HE MUST BE SOUGHT OUT AND DESTROYED!

BUT THE MESSAGE THAT HAD DISTRACTED THE MEKON FROM HIS SAVAGE ATTACK ON MEKONTA HAD ACTUALLY BEEN TRANSMITTED BY TECHNICIAN COB — A FRIEND OF DAN DARE!

IT SEEMS AS THOUGH I'VE DONE A USEFUL BIT OF TAMPERING WITH THIS TREEN TRANSMITTING GEAR — HERE COMES THE MEKON, JUST AS I ORDERED!

THERE LURKS AN EARTHMAN IN THE FORBIDDEN HALLS OF VENUS! KILL HIM!

BUT THE EARTHMAN DID NOT WAIT FOR DEATH!

CORNER HIM — KILL HIM — WHILE I PUNISH THE ONE WHO ALLOWED THIS MACHINERY TO DECEIVE US!

MEANWHILE, IN ANOTHER PART OF THE CAVERNS, DAN DARE GAZED DOWN AT WHERE ONE OF THE LAST THREE HAD FALLEN...

DEAD! HIS NECK IS BROKEN!

NOW LEADERLESS, THE VILE RED TREENS CRINGED BACK INTO THE MURK, WHILE DAN SOUGHT ESCAPE FROM THE BREEDING-HOUSE OF EVIL!

AFTER A CLIMB OF SEVERAL MINUTES...

THE FOUNDRY — AND THERE'S THE FIRST OF THE LAST THREE!

HUNTING THE SAME VICTIM, DAN DARE AND THE MEKON CAME FACE TO FACE!

THE MEKON!

DAN DARE! IT IS FITTING THAT YOU SHOULD DIE ON VENUS, BY MY HAND!

A BLOB OF FLAME SWIRLED AT DAN DARE!

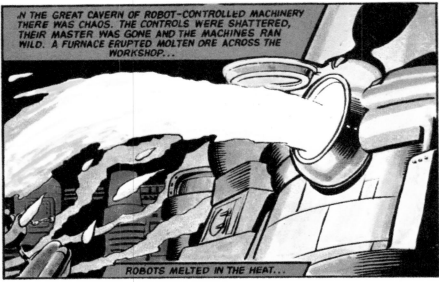

IN THE GREAT CAVERN OF ROBOT-CONTROLLED MACHINERY THERE WAS CHAOS. THE CONTROLS WERE SHATTERED, THEIR MASTER WAS GONE AND THE MACHINES RAN WILD. A FURNACE ERUPTED MOLTEN ORE ACROSS THE WORKSHOP...

ROBOTS MELTED IN THE HEAT...

DAN SAW THE MEKON SAIL INTO THE DARKNESS ABOVE THE WREATHING SMOKE...

HE KNOWS A WAY OUT! I MUST FOLLOW HIM!

DAN SCRAMBLED INTO THE GLOOM WITH FIRE DANCING AT HIS HEELS...

THERE'S THE MEKON AHEAD! HE SEEMS TO BE STOPPING!

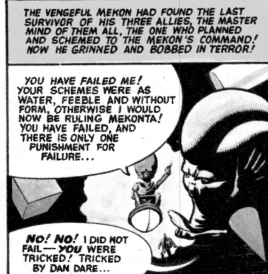

THE VENGEFUL MEKON HAD FOUND THE LAST SURVIVOR OF HIS THREE ALLIES, THE MASTER MIND OF THEM ALL, THE ONE WHO PLANNED AND SCHEMED TO THE MEKON'S COMMAND! NOW HE GRINNED AND BOBBED IN TERROR!

YOU HAVE FAILED ME! YOUR SCHEMES WERE AS WATER, FEEBLE AND WITHOUT FORM, OTHERWISE I WOULD NOW BE RULING MEKONTA! YOU HAVE FAILED, AND THERE IS ONLY ONE PUNISHMENT FOR FAILURE...

NO! NO! I DID NOT FAIL— YOU WERE TRICKED! TRICKED BY DAN DARE...

EEEEE-AAAAGH!

GOOD GRIEF!

THE MEKON SWIVELLED IN THE BITTER-TASTING AIR...

NOW, DAN DARE, YOU WILL DIE AT MY LEISURE— FOR YOU HAVE BEEN THE REPEATED CURSE OF MY PLANS!

SUDDENLY...

EEEEGH!

A THOUSAND TONS OF ROCK FOLLOWED THE MEKON INTO THE MIST, AND AFTER THE ROCK CAME RUBBLE AND DUST, THEN GREY VENUSIAN SUNLIGHT—AND SWIFT-MOVING BUZZING THERON MACHINES!

AND FROM ONE OF THE MACHINES CAME THE JOYFUL LANCASTRIAN VOICE OF ALBERT FITZWILLIAM DIGBY!

CAN YOU SEE THE MEKON?

NO, BUT BY GUM, I CAN SEE COLONEL DAN!

WE WERE IN A FLEET OF BIG SHIPS ON OUR WAY TO MEKONTA WHEN WE SAW THE MEKON. WE FOLLOWED HIM IN, HELPED COB OUT OF SOME TROUBLE, BUT GOT BLOCKED BY A FIRE, SO WE BLASTED OUR WAY IN FROM THE TOP— BUT COB THOUGHT THAT YOU WERE DEAD!

I'M NOT, BUT I THINK THE MEKON IS— YOU KNOCKED THE ROOF IN ON TOP OF HIM!

A FEW MINUTES LATER, THE THREE EARTHMEN WERE UNITED ABOARD A THERON SHIP. BEHIND THEM, DELAYED ACTION BOMBS AND THE NATURAL VOLCANIC NATURE OF THE FLAME LANDS COMBINED IN AN ATOMIC-SIZED EXPLOSION.

THAT'S THE END OF THE MEKON'S BOLT-HOLE, AND THE END OF ANOTHER ADVENTURE!

AND LET US HOPE THAT IT'S THE BEGINNING OF A NEW ERA OF PEACE ON VENUS AND THE EARTH!

IT'S FREE INSIDE!

EAGLE
AND Boys' World

24 October 1964   VOL. 15 No. 43   EVERY WEDNESDAY   6d.

DAN DARE
in a great new adventure
THE MUSHROOM

Although rushing through space at ten thousand miles an hour, it seemed no more than a speck against the black cloth of a billion timeless stars. It was a thing worked by a mind of its own. It was a machine that spat a tiny pellet of molten flame . . .

WAKE UP, SPACEMAN!

COLONEL DAN DARE, HERO OF THE SPACEWAYS, AND HIS BATMAN, ALBERT DIGBY, WERE ON ROVING PATROL IN THEIR SPACECRAFT—ANASTASIA . . .

EH? ER—OH, SORRY, SIR! JUST RESTING MY EYES FOR A FEW MOMENTS – THIS IS ONLY A ROUTINE PATROL. NOTHING'S HAPPENED, HAS IT?

AT THAT INSTANT, THE SHIP'S RADAR-LINKED SERVO-COMPUTERS ROLLED THE ANASTASIA OFF COURSE . . .

WHEEEE – OUCH! METEOR INVASION – THAT WAS A CLOSE ONE!

DIGBY'S 'METEOR' WAS IN FACT TO BECOME A DEADLY INSTRUMENT OF TERROR, FOR IT HAD BEEN CREATED BY ONE WHOM THEY HAD THOUGHT DEAD – THE SINISTER ARCH-ENEMY OF ALL MANKIND – THE MEKON!

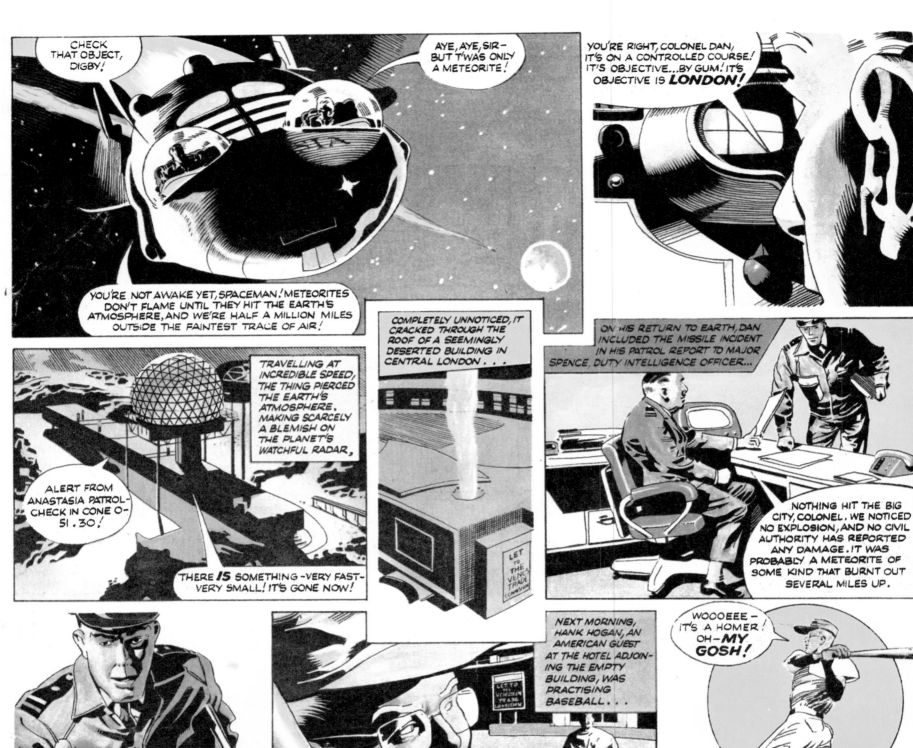

ANOTHER GREAT EXTRA!

EAGLE
AND Boys' World

31 October 1964 Vol. 15 No. 44 • EVERY WEDNESDAY • 6d.

DAN DARE
Pilot of the Future
in THE MUSHROOM

After a routine flight in outer space, Dan Dare had reported seeing a tiny, flaming missile flying at great speed towards London. Although the missile had secretly come to rest in the Venusian Trade Commission building, his report was ignored. But later, when an American space official – Hank Hogan – went to retrieve his baseball from the building . . .

THE TEMPERATURE IN THE ROOM WAS WELL BELOW ZERO – AND IT SEEMED TO BE SUDDENLY LOWERED BY THE ICY STARES OF TREEN HATE THAT STABBED AT THE INTRUDER...

O.K., FELLERS, SORRY TO INTERRUPT — I ONLY CAME FOR MY BALL!

HEY, LAY OFF WILL YOU, YOU GREEN GOOKS! YOU CAN'T DO THIS TO ME — I'M AN AMERICAN CITIZEN!

AS HANK WAS TOSSED OUT OF THE BUILDING, THE WEIRD SPACE-CRAFT THAT HAD FIRED THE MUSHROOM SEED WAS NOW EMITTING A STRANGE BUT POWERFUL RADIATION THOUSANDS OF MILES OUT IN SPACE...

MEANWHILE, DAN DARE HAD BEEN MAKING A DETERMINED EFFORT TO SOLVE THE MYSTERY OF THE WEIRD MISSILE HE HAD OBSERVED BLAZING THROUGH SPACE TOWARDS LONDON!

SORRY, COLONEL, WE'VE HAD NOTHING REPORTED IN THAT LINE OF TROUBLE...

EVENTUALLY HE CALLED ON THE COMMISSIONER OF POLICE...

IS THERE NOTHING AT ALL, NO MATTER HOW TRIVIAL, THAT CAN'T BE EXPLAINED?

THERE WAS AN AMERICAN WHO CLAIMED, IN HIS OWN WORDS, TO HAVE BEEN 'EJECTED OUT OF SOME TWO-BIT TREEN DREAMLAND'. BUT THE BUILDING IN QUESTION IS BEYOND OUR JURISDICTION, THE SAME AS A FOREIGN EMBASSY, SO WE COULD DO NOTHING ABOUT CAPTAIN HANK HOGAN'S COMPLAINT!

BY GUM, THAT'S OUR OLD PAL HANK!

YOUR PAL, EH? WELL HE MADE A TREMENDOUS FUSS OVER NOTHING!

HANK IS TOO EASY-GOING TO MAKE A FUSS — UNLESS IT WERE FOR A VERY URGENT REASON!

EEE — IT'LL BE JUST LIKE OLD TIMES, MEETING HANK AGAIN!

HELI-PARK
NEW WASHINGTON
NEW WASHINGTON HOTEL

KEITH WATSON

A FEW MINUTES LATER...

IT'S GOOD TO SEE YOU, HANK!

AND YOU, DANNY BOY. A LONG TIME NO SEE, EH?

IT TURNED OUT THAT THE TEXAN HAD KEPT IN TOUCH WITH ALL THEIR COMRADES FROM PAST ADVENTURES...

...PIERRE LAFAYETTE, HE'S NOW PRINCIPAL OF THE LAKE CHAD ROCKETRY COLLEGE. HE SAYS IT GIVES HIM OPPORTUNITIES FOR PILOTING, FISHING AND FRENCH COOKING! O'MALLEY'S CONTROLLING SOME SEA-HARVEST PROJECT IN THE INDIAN OCEAN. AS YOU KNOW, SIR HUBERT HAS RETIRED — HIS MEMOIRS ARE SOON DUE FOR PUBLICATION...

AND MISS PEABODY — THE PROFESSOR, I MEAN...?

YOU MEAN MRS JACK GURK! SHE MARRIED A MINING ENGINEER AND MOVED WITH HIM TO ONE OF THE MARTIAN COLONIES. SHE'S DONE GREAT WORK UP THERE PLANNING A CROP ROTATION FOR THE MARTIAN SOIL!

AS THE FRIENDS RECALLED TIMES PAST, THE SINISTER TREENS IN THE NEXT BUILDING ARRIVED AT A POINT IN THE MEKON'S PLAN THAT WOULD AFFECT THE WHOLE FUTURE OF LONDON — AND EARTH!

PHASE THREE IMMINENT! ALL TREENS MOVE TO DUTY POSITIONS!

UNAWARE OF THE FRENZIED ACTIVITY IN THE NEARBY VENUS TRADE COMMISSION BUILDING, DAN AT LAST TURNED THE CONVERSATION ON TO THE MAIN PURPOSE OF HIS CALL!

NOW TELL US ABOUT THOSE TREENS ACROSS THE WAY, HANK

FOR ONE THING, THEY THREW ME OUT — AND I THOUGHT TREENS WERE ALLOWED HERE ON EARTH BECAUSE THEY WERE UNDER ORDERS TO BE FRIENDLY! BUT THERE'S MORE TO IT THAN THAT...

GREAT SCOTT!

GURGLING GALAXIES — IT'S THE MUSHROOM!

EAGLE
AND Boys' World

7 November 1964   VOL. 15 No. 45   EVERY WEDNESDAY   6d.

DAN DARE
Pilot of the Future
in THE MUSHROOM

Although the world believed that the evil Mekon of Venus was dead, he had fired a mysterious missile at the Earth and it had entered a large deserted building in central London. Dan Dare had seen the missile streaking through space, but did not know where it had landed — until it had grown into an immense 'mushroom' of glowing metal!

THE DUST BEGAN TO SETTLE AND LONDONERS RAN TOWARDS THE THING TO GAPE AT IT IN WIDE-EYED WONDER!

WHAT IS IT? WHERE DID IT COME FROM?

SOMEONE MAY BE BURIED UNDER THAT RUBBLE!

THE BUILDING WAS EMPTY!

BUT LONDON'S LAW WAS SOON THERE TO RESTORE ORDER AND CALM TO THE AGITATED CITIZENS...

NOW JUST KEEP CALM, EVERYBODY! AND KEEP AWAY TILL WE KNOW WHAT'S REALLY HAPPENED!

NOW, JUST KEEP BACK, EVERYONE, PLEASE.

EXCUSE ME — LET ME THROUGH, PLEASE!

SORRY, COLONEL DARE, SIR! I DIDN'T RECOGNIZE YOU AT FIRST!

DAN DARE TOOK CHARGE OF THE SITUATION...

CLEAR THE AREA, CONSTABLE. DIGBY, CALL COLONEL BANGER — HE'S THE SCIENTIFIC EXPERT. THAT MUSHROOM IS PROBABLY DANGEROUS AND WE'LL NEED ALL THE HELP WE CAN MUSTER!

DIGBY USED A PUBLIC VIDEOPHONE...

IT'S ALL METAL—RED HOT IN PLACES—BUT IT'S GROWN THERE LIKE A PLANT!

A FRIEND OF OURS, HANK HOGAN, SAW IT WHEN IT WAS SMALLER, AND HE SAID IT WAS BEING TENDED BY TREENS!

A few alien Treens were always allowed into London under licence, and generally they lived as peacefully as any other citizens. Now, it seemed, *some Treens had gone bad!* At the moment, they were out of sight within the strange growth, drawing on molten soft rods of metal that were pushed up from the roots...

...AND DRAGGING THEM INTO POSITION WITHIN THE ALREADY SPREADING UMBRELLA...

OTHERS BENT FINER STRANDS OF METAL TO FORM COMPLEX CIRCUITS OF STILL MORE DEVICES.

And, far away in outer space, the Mekon, Lord of the Treens in their bygone age of warlike ambition and savagery, and the evil genius who hated all mankind, was informed in detail of their progress . . .

ALL GOES WELL WITH YOUR PLAN, MASTER!

THEN LONDON WILL SOON BE AT MY MERCY!

SUDDENLY, THERE WAS A WAILING IN THE LONDON SKIES...

HERE COMES BANGER— I WONDER WHAT HE'LL MAKE OF THIS THING!

BANGER LEAPED FROM THE AIRCRAFT BEFORE IT SETTLED DOWN AND WAVED A COUPLE OF MEN UP THE SLOPE OF BROKEN CEMENT...

ANY IDEA WHAT THIS THING IS?

NO! AND I'M TAKING NO CHANCES! I'VE CHECKED AT HIGH LEVEL AND PERSUADED THEM THAT THE BEST THING TO DO IS TO BLOW IT TO PIECES.

IF WE DESTROY THIS THING AND WE'RE WRONG, WE CAN APOLOGIZE LATER! BUT I'D SOONER USE EXPLOSIVES NOW, THAN WAIT TO FIND OUT THAT...

THE MEN ARE HURT—THEY'RE FALLING!

THERE WAS NO SHOT— NOTHING! WHAT'S HAPPENED TO THEM?

AAAAGH!

EAGLE
AND Boys' World
14 November 1964 Vol. 15 No. 46 · EVERY WEDNESDAY · 6d.

DAN DARE
Pilot of the Future
in THE MUSHROOM

The Mekon, arch-enemy of mankind, had fired a pellet from deep space. It had landed in the heart of London and grown into a strange, gigantic mushroom. Dan Dare saw it destroy one building. Then two men with explosives approached the massive stem – and collapsed without apparent cause!

THEY'RE FROZEN STIFF!

A DOCTOR CONFIRMED DAN DARE'S ASTOUNDING DIAGNOSIS . . .

ACUTE CASES OF FROSTBITE. I'D SAY IT WAS IMPOSSIBLE IN TODAY'S TEMPERATURE OF FIFTEEN CENTIGRADE IN THE SHADE – BUT FROSTBITTEN THEY ARE!

THAT THING'S THE CAUSE OF IT!

I'VE MORE EXPLOSIVES – DO YOU THINK WE SHOULD PERSIST IN TRYING THEM?

I THINK SO, WILF! BUT THEY'LL HAVE TO BE LOBBED OR FIRED AT THE THING. WE CAN'T RISK ANY MORE MEN!

HIGH-VELOCITY GRENADES WERE LOADED INTO THE TEAR GAS MORTARS OF A POLICE HELICOPTER . . .

LET'S HOPE THIS DOES THE TRICK!

THE BOMBS WOBBLED TOWARDS THEIR LOATHSOME TARGET, THEN SEEMED TO STRIKE AN INVISIBLE BARRIER AND BOUNCED BACK!

EVERYBODY— DOWN!

KEITH WATSON

THAT THING IS WELL EQUIPPED TO DEFEND ITSELF, SO WHAT'S OUR NEXT MOVE, DAN?

TO FIND OUT WHERE IT CAME FROM AND WHY! TO BEGIN WITH, I WANT THIS MUSHROOM THING EXAMINED WITH EVERY AVAILABLE DEVICE!

THE CALL WENT OUT, AND EXPERTS FROM EVERY FIELD OF SCIENCE CONVERGED UPON THE WEIRD STRUCTURE NOW BEGINNING TO REAR ABOVE THE ROOF TOPS . . .

DAN MADE A KEEN EXAMINATION OF THE SURVEYORS' FINDINGS . . .

INFRA-RED PHOTOGRAPHY REVEALED THIS BEACON DIRECTED ON TO THE MUSHROOM. WE'VE ALSO NOTICED THAT ITS DIRECTION VARIES SLIGHTLY FROM TIME TO TIME!

THEN PLOT THE VARIATIONS AND LET ME HAVE THE RESULT AS SOON AS POSSIBLE—DIGBY, CONTACT SPACEFLEET H.Q. AND TELL THEM TO ROLL OUT ANASTASIA. WE'LL TRACK THAT BEACON TO ITS SOURCE!

IN FACT, THE SOURCE WAS A STRANGE OBJECT IN ORBIT FAR BEYOND THE MOON!

IT WAS A DEVICE CONTROLLED BY THE LORD OF TERROR HIMSELF—THE EVIL, GREEN-SKINNED MEKON!

IS THERE PANIC AND FEAR IN THE CITY YET?

NO, MASTER, THERE IS MUCH ACTIVITY, BUT NO SIGN OF FEAR!

LONDONERS TAKE A PRIDE IN THEIR CALMNESS IN TIMES OF TROUBLE—BUT SOON THEIR PRIDE WILL BE BROKEN, AND THEY WILL BE FLEEING IN TERROR!

EAGLE
AND Boys' World

21 November 1964 VOL. 15 No. 47 EVERY WEDNESDAY 6d.

DAN DARE
Pilot of the Future
in THE MUSHROOM

The evil Mekon had caused a great metallic mushroom to grow in the heart of London, and it had already destroyed one large building. Dan Dare had decided to track an infra-red beam that shone upon the destructive mushroom from outer space . . .

THE ANASTASIA—SPACE-BOUND!

DAN NOSED THE ANASTASIA TOWARDS LONDON AND THE OMINOUS MENACE THAT NOW GREW IN ITS HEART!

THERE IT IS, DIGBY! TURN ON THE INFRA-RED FILTER AND SEE IF WE CAN FIND THE BEACON!

INFRA-RED COMING UP, SIR!

THE BEACON'S SHOWING UP CLEAR ENOUGH, SIR!

I WONDER WHAT WE'LL FIND AT THE END OF THIS INFRA-RED RAINBOW!

BUT AS DAN DARE HEADED FOR SPACE...

HEY—STEADY THERE!

THE GROUND'S TREMBLING—IT'S AN EARTHQUAKE!

WITHOUT FURTHER WARNING, A GREAT FISSURE CRACKED OPEN...

THEN CAME THE COLLAPSE AS EARTH FELL INTO THE WIDENING GAP, AND DRAGGED ONE SIDE OF THE HOTEL IN AFTER IT!

JUMPING MERCURY BEANS — WE HOPPED BACK OUT OF TROUBLE NOT A SECOND TOO SOON, EH, COLONEL?

THIS WHOLE AREA MUST BE TOTALLY EVACUATED BEFORE MORE BUILDINGS COLLAPSE. IT SEEMS THAT THE MUSHROOM IS DRAWING ITS RAW MATERIALS FROM THE SOIL — HENCE THE SUBSIDENCE!

AND IT ALSO SEEMS TO DRAW EVERY POSSIBLE THERM OF HEAT FROM THE EARTH, TOO, THE WHOLE REACTION SEEMINGLY STIMULATED BY THAT BEAM DAN DARE'S FOLLOWING!

DAN DARE HAD CUT THE ANASTASIA'S BOOSTER ROCKETS AND WAS FOLLOWING THE BEAM ON NORMAL IMPULSE MOTORS...

ON COURSE, SIR— WE'RE RIDING RIGHT ALONG THE BEAM!

BUT THE SINISTER GREEN MASTER-MIND WHO HAD CREATED THIS EVIL CONTRIVANCE WAS WARNED OF THE ANASTASIA'S APPROACH...

O, MASTER, THE MUSHROOM CONTINUES ITS RATE OF GROWTH ACCORDING TO PLAN!

REPORT, O' MASTER, OF EARTH SHIP APPROACHING ALONG STIMULUS BEAM!

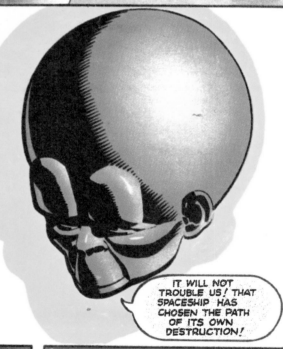

IT WILL NOT TROUBLE US! THAT SPACESHIP HAS CHOSEN THE PATH OF ITS OWN DESTRUCTION!

ABOUT THAT TIME, ONE OF THE DIALS ON THE ANASTASIA'S PANEL BEGAN TO SHOW AN ABNORMAL READING!

EEEH, THAT'S RUM, SIR! THERE'S AN INCREASE IN THE ANNIE'S SKIN TEMPERATURE!

CHECK THE REFRIGERATION UNIT — MAYBE IT'S FAILED!

DIGBY CHECKED...

THE REFRIGERATION IS WORKING AT FULL OUTPUT! BUT BY GUM, SIR, WE'RE WELL CLEAR OF THE EARTH'S ATMOSPHERE...

...THERE SHOULD BE NO FRICTION TO CAUSE THE HEAT!

THEN IT'S THE BEAM! WE'LL SWING OUT OF IT AND RIDE PARALLEL!

BUT...

THE ANNIE'S NOT RESPONDING TO THE CONTROLS! WE'RE TRAPPED IN THE BEAM!

AND THE OUTSIDE TEMPERATURE'S INCREASING— WE'LL BURN UP!

EAGLE
AND Boys' World

28 November 1964 Vol. 15 No. 48 — EVERY WEDNESDAY — 6d.

DAN DARE
Pilot of the Future
in THE MUSHROOM

Dan Dare and Digby were in the spaceship *Anastasia*, rushing along a beamed ray that had stimulated a great metallic mushroom to grow in London. The whole thing was devised by the evil Mekon. Suddenly, Dan Dare realized that they were trapped in the beam, that had already heated the *Anastasia's* skin to a fantastic temperature . . .

THERE'S NO RESPONSE TO THE CONTROLS—AND THE OUTSIDE TEMPERATURE MUST BE COLOSSAL!

BY GUM, I'M BEGINNING TO FEEL LIKE A LAMB CHOP ON A GRILL!

THERE IS JUST A CHANCE THAT WE CAN GET OUT OF THIS HOT-SPOT!

THIS HEAT AND THE HOLDING RAY MAY BE A DEFENCE AGAINST NORMAL SPACESHIPS ON NORMAL IMPULSE MOTORS! I'M GOING TO STOP THEM AND SEE WHAT HAPPENS!

IMPULSE MOTORS OUT!

THEN DAN SWITCHED IN THE MAGNETIC MOTORS—A SYSTEM ALMOST UNIQUE TO THERON SHIPS AND THE ANASTASIA! THERE WAS A COMFORTING LURCH AS THE NEW POWER SYSTEM TOOK OVER...

WE'RE ON MAGNETIC—NOW LET'S TRY THE CONTROLS!

EAGLE

AND Boys' World

5 December 1964   VOL. 15 No. 49   EVERY WEDNESDAY   6d.

DAN DARE
Pilot of the Future
in THE MUSHROOM

Dan Dare and Digby, in the spacecraft *Anastasia*, were heading for a distant artificial satellite that had stimulated the growth of an uncanny metal 'mushroom' in the centre of London. It was from the satellite that the evil Mekon interrupted *all* tele-communications to deliver his ultimatum . . .

I DEMAND THAT ALL EARTH SETTLEMENTS BE REMOVED FROM VENUS AT ONCE! I DEMAND TO BE RESTORED TO FULL CONTROL OF MEKONTA—OR LONDON WILL BE UTTERLY DESTROYED!

KEITH WATSON

FAMILIES EVERYWHERE DISCUSSED THIS NERVE-SHATTERING INTRUSION...

WHAT IS THIS PROGRAMME?

SOME KIND OF NEWSFLASH!

IT'S THE MEKON THREATENING TO KILL US ALL UNLESS WE GIVE HIM BACK VENUS!

THE ULTIMATUM WAS ALSO DISCUSSED IN 'HIGH PLACES'...

SUPPOSING WE ACCEPT HIS TERMS, PRIME MINISTER?

IT WOULD ONLY BE A MATTER OF TIME BEFORE THE MEKON WOULD USE VENUS AS A BASE FOR A FULL-SCALE INVASION OF THE EARTH!

WE MUST RESIST! IF IT BECOMES NECESSARY FOR THE SAFETY OF THE REST OF THE WORLD, THEN LONDON WILL BE SACRIFICED!

BUT FAR OUT IN SPACE, DAN DARE HAD AT LAST ARRIVED WITHIN SIGHT OF THE EVIL SATELLITE...

THERE'S THE SOURCE OF THE TROUBLE, DIGBY!

BY HECK—IT'S A QUEER OBJECT!

REPORT OUR POSITION TO CONTROL, AND TELL THEM WE'RE GOING RIGHT ALONGSIDE THE THING!

BUT AS THE ANASTASIA PASSED BETWEEN THE GREAT SHIELDS, SOME FANTASTIC UNSEEN FORCE SPUN THE SPACECRAFT LIKE A SILVER TOP!

DAN DARE AND DIGBY WERE HURLED FROM THEIR SEATS!

THE VIOLENT MOTION EASED, BUT THE MEN WERE LEFT SPRAWLED AND HELPLESS INSIDE THE TRAPPED SPACECRAFT...

I-I CAN'T MOVE! IT'S AS THOUGH MY LIMBS WERE MADE OF WOOD! WHAT'S HAPPENED?

I DON'T KNOW, DIGBY! I DON'T KNOW!

THE ANASTASIA'S ARRIVAL WAS REPORTED INSIDE THE METAL CORE OF THE STRANGE SATELLITE...

O MASTER, THERE IS AN INTRUDER WITHIN OUR ZONE OF FORCE!

THEN DESTROY THE OBSTRUCTION, WHATEVER IT MAY BE!

TWO OF THE MEKON'S TREENS EMERGED FROM THE SATELLITE TO DO THEIR MASTER'S BIDDING. THEY WERE CLAD IN SPECIAL SUITS THAT INSULATED THEM FROM THE ZONE OF FORCE THAT HAD NUMBED THE LIMBS OF DAN AND DIGBY...

WAIT! I RECOGNIZE THAT AS THE ANASTASIA! IF THE FAMOUS EARTH PILOT DAN DARE IS AT THE CONTROLS, WE HAVE A CHANCE OF EARNING THE ETERNAL PRAISE OF OUR MASTER!

THE TREENS ENTERED THE ANASTASIA AND COMPRESSED THE NUMBED OCCUPANTS INTO SPACE SUITS...

THIS FAT ONE DOES NOT FIT EASILY INTO A SUIT! IS IT NECESSARY THAT WE BOTHER TO DELIVER HIM ALIVE?

THE MEKON WILL GIVE US MUCH HONOUR WHEN WE PRESENT HIM WITH. BOTH PRISONERS TO DEAL WITH IN HIS OWN WAY!

THE TREENS TOWED THEIR CAPTIVES ACROSS THE INTERVENING SPACE AND DOWN INTO THE HEART OF THE SPHERE WHERE THEY TRIUMPHANTLY DISPLAYED THEM TO THEIR EVIL MASTER!

O MASTER! THE OBSTRUCTION WAS CAUSED BY YOUR ENEMY—DAN DARE!

I ORDERED YOU TO DESTROY THE OBSTRUCTION! YOU HAVE DISOBEYED MY ORDER—THE PUNISHMENT FOR DISOBEDIENCE IS DEATH!

THE TREENS DIED, AND DAN DARE AND DIGBY HELPLESSLY FACED THE MURDEROUS, SNAKE-LIKE EYES OF THE MEKON!

EAGLE AND Boys' World

12 December 1964 Vol. 15 No. 50

EVERY WEDNESDAY

6d.

DAN DARE

Pilot of the Future

in THE MUSHROOM

Dan Dare and Digby had arrived on a strange satellite that had stimulated the growth of an uncanny metal mushroom in the heart of London. This satellite, they discovered, was controlled by the Mekon. Due to the effects of a mysterious field of force, Dan and Digby were unable to move, and were at the mercy of the Mekon!

STAND THEM BEFORE A MONITOR SCREEN SO THAT THEY MAY WATCH THE DESTRUCTION OF LONDON BEFORE THEY DIE!

THE VILE GREEN CREATURE FROM VENUS HOVERED TAUNTINGLY, INCHES BEFORE DAN'S EYES!

YOU ARE PARALYSED IN EVERY MUSCLE, AND YOU SHALL REMAIN SO LONG ENOUGH TO WITNESS MY FIRST DEVASTATING BLOW AGAINST EARTH!

THE FIEND! NOW HE'S GIVING ORDERS TO THAT MUSHROOM THING IN THE HEART OF LONDON!

INSIDE THE OMINOUS METAL SHAPE, A SQUAD OF THE MEKON'S TREENS RECEIVED THEIR SINISTER MASTER'S COMMANDS...

BEGIN PHASE FOUR!

WE HEAR AND OBEY, O MASTER!

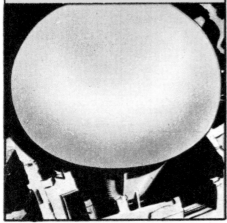

ALTHOUGH THE MUSHROOM LOOKED THE SAME FROM THE OUTSIDE, ITS INTERIOR WAS NOW BUZZING WITH FEVERISH ACTIVITY...

MISSILE HEADS POKED DOWN THROUGH ITS APERTURES, SILENT AND OMINOUS IN THEIR INTENT!

COLONEL BANGER, NOW IN CHARGE OF GROUND DEFENCE AROUND THE MUSHROOM, WATCHED, HIS JAW SET GRIMLY...

WHAT'S HAPPENING NOW, COLONEL?

SEEMS AS THOUGH THEY'RE LOWERING MISSILES OF SOME KIND! WE'RE IN FOR TROUBLE...

HERE IT COMES... GET DOWN!

LONDON SHUDDERED UNDER THE IMPACT OF THIS FIRST, DEVASTATING SALVO, BUT COLONEL WILF BANGER SPOKE INTO HIS WRIST-MICROPHONE, CALLING FOR SWIFT RETALIATION...

OPERATION BREAKFAST! LET'S FRY THAT MUSHROOM!

THE ORDER WAS TRANSMITTED TO A ROCKET BATTERY IN RICHMOND PARK...

THERE THEY GO, HANK!

ATTABOY! GET IN THERE AND BEND THAT FUNGUS!

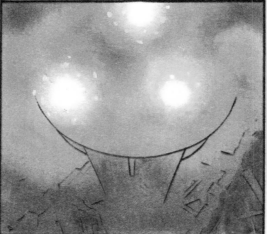

EVERY MISSILE BURST ON TARGET, RELEASING ENOUGH CONTROLLED NUCLEAR HEAT TO INCINERATE EVERY SUBSTANCE SO FAR KNOWN TO MAN!

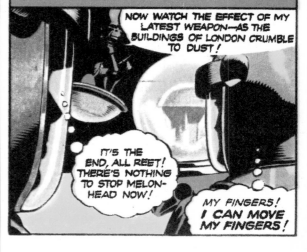

AND THOUSANDS OF MILES AWAY, DIGBY GROANED INWARDLY AT THE SIGHT OF THE UNMARKED METAL MUSHROOM, BUT DAN DARE'S EYES WERE ALIVE WITH INNER HOPE!

NOW WATCH THE EFFECT OF MY LATEST WEAPON—AS THE BUILDINGS OF LONDON CRUMBLE TO DUST!

IT'S THE END, ALL REET! THERE'S NOTHING TO STOP MELON-HEAD NOW!

MY FINGERS! I CAN MOVE MY FINGERS!

SECONDS LATER, A BLUE SWORD OF LIGHT STABBED FROM 'THE MUSHROOM,' SLICING ACROSS THE LONDON ROOFTOPS...

SCORCHED FACADES CRUMBLED BENEATH THE INTENSITY OF THAT SEARING GLARE!

COLONEL WILF BANGER, OFFICER IN COMMAND OF GROUND DEFENCE, WATCHED IN FURY AND DESPAIR...

THE DEVILS ARE USING A HEAT RAY!

THERE'S NO DEFENCE AGAINST A THING LIKE THAT!

THE MEKON HAD THE ADVANTAGE AND, WITH CALCULATED CRUELTY, HE BROKE IN ON TV PROGRAMMES, HIS FEARSOME IMAGE APPEARING SUDDENLY ON COUNTLESS SCREENS IN SUBURBAN HOMES...

I AM BURNING CENTRAL LONDON WITH A HEAT RAY WITH AN EFFECTIVE RANGE OF TWENTY-FIVE MILES!

AS THE GREEN MENACE EXPECTED, THERE WAS SUDDEN PANIC AND FEAR IN THE SUBURBS...

THE MEKON'S COMING— TO BURN DOWN OUR HOMES!

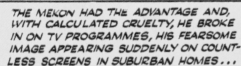

SOON THE AIR WAS FILLED WITH THE THROB OF ESCAPING MACHINES!

ENFIELD SKY-CONTROL

IT'S LIKE A BEES' NEST GONE MAD OUT THERE!

THE MEKON TURNED FROM HIS VIDEO VIEW OF THE SCENE WITH MALICIOUS SATISFACTION!

THE PEOPLE ARE BLIND WITH FEAR! THEY WILL SOON DEMAND THAT THEIR GOVERNMENT RESTORES ME TO POWER ON VENUS!

I CAN MOVE MY ARMS— IT'S NOW OR NEVER!

DAN JERKED TO LIFE. HIS LIMBS, THOUGH CLUMSY, MOVED AS SWIFTLY AS PISTONS...

EEEEK!

THOUGH HIS NUMB LEGS REFUSED TO SUPPORT HIM, DAN GRIPPED THE WRITHING MEKON:

STOP THAT HEAT RAY— OR ELSE!

UUUURGH! STOP.. UG.. THE RAY.. STOP PHASE FIVE —UUURK!

BUT AS THE COMMAND WAS OBEYED...

MASTER, IF YOU ARE HARMED, SHALL I KILL THE EARTHMAN DIGBY?

EAGLE
AND Boys' World

26 December 1964 Vol. 15 No. 52 · EVERY WEDNESDAY · 6d.

DAN DARE
Pilot of the Future

in THE MUSHROOM

The Mekon had begun a systematic destruction of London from a satellite far out in space that transmitted power to an immense metal mushroom which had grown in the heart of the city. Inside the satellite, Dan Dare had snatched the Mekon from his hovering saucer, but . . .

IT IS STALEMATE, DAN DARE! IF YOU HARM ME — YOUR FRIEND WILL DIE!

DIGBY SPOKE UP AT ONCE. HE SPOKE WORDS OF GREAT COURAGE – HIS VOICE WAS FIRM...

DON'T WORRY ABOUT WHAT HAPPENS TO ME, SIR! TAKE THE CHANCE TO RID THE WORLD OF THE MEKON AND ALL THE EVIL CONNECTED WITH HIS NAME!

BUT DAN DARE WOULD NOT HAZARD THE LIFE OF A FRIEND SO EASILY. HE HESITATED — AND IN THAT VITAL INSTANT...

LOOK OUT, SIR!

ALTHOUGH UNSEATED, THE MEKON COULD CONTROL HIS FLYING CHAIR BY IMPULSES FROM HIS POWERFUL, OVER-SIZED BRAIN...

AAAH!

FOOLS! YOU FORGET THAT I CONTROL THE MOVEMENTS OF MY CHAIR BY THOUGHT-WAVES!

THE SUBURBS WERE EMPTYING. THE MEKON HAD THREATENED TO DESTROY ALL HOMES, UNLESS HIS DEMAND TO BE RESTORED TO POWER ON VENUS WAS GRANTED...

I AWAIT YOUR COMMAND TO RESUME PHASE FIVE, O MASTER!

FIRST LET ME SEE IF IT IS NECESSARY TO CONTINUE THE ATTACK!

THE MEKON FOCUSED ONE OF HIS VIDEO SCREENS ON THE SHATTERED HEART OF LONDON...

THE DAMAGE IS NOT GREAT —— BUT IT IS SPECTACULAR!

THEN HE SWITCHED HIS VIEW TO THE SUBURBS, A SCENE OF FEAR AND FRANTIC CONFUSION...

EMERGENCY EXIT ROUTE B6

ONCE AGAIN, THE MEKON AND HIS TREENS COULD DEVOTE ALL THEIR VILE ATTENTION TO THE ASSAULT ON LONDON!

WHAT ARE WE GOING TO DO?

FIGHT BACK!

HEAR! HEAR!

WE CAN'T FIGHT THAT MUSHROOM! IT'S INDESTRUCTIBLE!

THE MEKON HAS ASKED FOR VENUS!

THEN GIVE IT TO HIM, I SAY! I DON'T CARE TWO BOTTLE-TOPS ABOUT VENUS —— BUT I CARE ABOUT MY HOME AND FAMILY!

BEFORE VERY LONG, DEPUTATIONS OF CHOSEN SUBURBAN CITIZENS MADE THEIR WAY TO DOWNING STREET...

WE WANT WOOD GREEN SO GIVE THE MEKON VENUS

BARNET SAYS BARGAIN!

THE PRIME MINISTER WATCHED THE DEMONSTRATION, HIS BROW HEAVY AS A THUNDER CLOUD!

WHAT DO WE DO, SIR GREGORY? DO WE BUY PEACE BY AGREEING TO RESTORE THE MEKON TO POWER ON VENUS?

TO DO THAT WOULD SIMPLY GIVE THE MEKON MORE RESOURCES FOR DESTRUCTION AND EVIL! WE MUST RESIST HIM TO THE LAST!

BUT THE MEKON SEEMED TO BELIEVE THAT THE PEOPLE WOULD BEND THE WILL OF AUTHORITY...

LONDON WILL SOON SUBMIT. NOW I MUST PREPARE OTHER CITIES TO YIELD TO MY DEMANDS!

YOU MEAN YOU INTEND TO DESTROY CITY AFTER CITY UNTIL THE WORLD GOVERNMENT AGREES TO YOUR DEMANDS? YOU INTEND TO KILL TENS OF THOUSANDS OF PEOPLE JUST TO WIN POWER FOR YOURSELF?

FOR ANSWER, THE MEKON FIRED A SECOND PELLET EARTHWARDS, KNOWING THAT IT WOULD ROOT AND GROW INTO ANOTHER INVINCIBLE MUSHROOM OF DOOM!

EAGLE
AND Boys' World

2 January 1965   VOL. 16 No. 1   EVERY WEDNESDAY   **6**d.

DAN DARE
Pilot of the Future

in THE MUSHROOM

The Mekon had caused a great destructive, metallic mushroom to grow in the heart of London. With Dan Dare and Digby prisoners on the satellite from which he controlled his 'power-plant', the Mekon fired another mushroom 'seed' towards the Earth . . .

THE FIERY PELLET PLUNGED EARTHWARDS...

THE PELLET HIT A DERELICT TENEMENT HOUSE IN OLD HARLEM, NEW YORK...

OTHER PELLETS FOLLOWED IN RAPID SEQUENCE—SECRETLY EMBEDDING THEM-SELVES IN THE HEARTS OF OTHER CITIES, SUCH AS DALLAS AND TOKYO...

...BOMBAY—PEKING—PARIS...

MEANWHILE, THE SEED THAT HAD BEEN PLANTED IN LONDON HAD DEVELOPED INTO A GROWTH OF HIDEOUS TERROR, SPREADING ICY FEAR AND DESTRUCTION WITH ITS EVER-EXPANDING HOOD!

PRIME MINISTER SIR GREGORY MOTTON AND HIS CABINET WERE AMONG THE FEW PEOPLE WHO REMAINED IN THE DESOLATE CITY...

THE WHOLE NATION IS ANXIOUS—PEOPLE ARE EVEN AFRAID FOR THEIR OWN LIVES, SIR GREGORY. HOW MUCH LONGER MUST WE HOLD OUT?

I'VE SENT FOR COLONEL BANGER. HE SHOULD ANSWER THAT QUESTION FOR US. LET HIM IN, HUSKINS!

YES, SIR!

COLONEL WILF BANGER WAS IN FIELD COMMAND OF DEFENCE AGAINST THE SEEMINGLY IMPREGNABLE MUSHROOM...

WE HAVE FOUND THAT GROUND AND AERIAL ATTACKS ARE USELESS, ONLY ONE APPROACH REMAINS—UNDERGROUND!

BY PACKING THE RIGHT PORTIONS OF THE UNDERGROUND RAILWAY TUNNELS AND THE LARGER SEWERS WITH EXPLOSIVES, WE COULD UNDERMINE THE WHOLE METALLIC STRUCTURE!

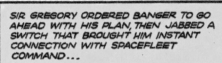

SIR GREGORY ORDERED BANGER TO GO AHEAD WITH HIS PLAN, THEN JABBED A SWITCH THAT BROUGHT HIM INSTANT CONNECTION WITH SPACEFLEET COMMAND...

ANY NEWS OF DAN DARE?

ONE HURRIED REPORT OF CONTACTING AN ALIEN SATELLITE—SINCE THEN, COMPLETE SILENCE!

WE FEAR THAT COLONEL DARE AND SPACEMAN DIGBY MAY BE...

DEAD? THEN IT'S CLEAR THAT THE SATELLITE IS HOSTILE AND MUST BE DESTROYED AT ONCE! DESPATCH WHATEVER SHIPS YOU CONSIDER NECESSARY FOR THE TASK—I'LL GET UNITED NATIONS CLEARANCE IMMEDIATELY!

IN FACT, DAN AND DIGBY WERE INSIDE THE ALIEN SATELLITE, PRISONERS OF THE MEKON...

SPACEFLEET HAS BEEN ALERTED, O MEKON! THE POOR FOOLS WILL DIE BEFORE THEY COME WITHIN TEN THOUSAND MILES OF HERE!

WHAT DO YOU WANT, MEKON? WHY ARE YOU CAUSING ALL THIS SLAUGHTER?

I WANT MY RIGHTFUL POWER AS RULER OF MEKONTA AND OF ALL THE TREENS OF VENUS! I WILL WIN MY DEMANDS—THE PEOPLE OF EARTH WILL HAND ME MY RIGHTS!

AND ONCE AGAIN THE MEKON IMPOSED HIS IMAGE ON ALL TELEVISION SCREENS WITHIN A WIDE RADIUS OF LONDON!

I HAVE DRIVEN YOU LONDONERS FROM YOUR HOMES. SOON, PEOPLE LIKE YOU WILL BE RUNNING FROM CITIES ALL OVER THE WORLD. MY POWER IS LIMITLESS, YOUR GOVERNMENT'S RESISTANCE IS FOOLISH...

EMERGENCY CAMPING SITE

SUDDENLY...

GIVE ME— EEEEEK!

THIS IS DAN DARE, CALLING SPACEFLEET H.Q. ...

WOW! JUST LOOK AT THAT!

THE MEKON CAN DESTROY ALL SPACESHIPS POWERED BY STANDARD IMPULSE MOTORS. SEND SHIPS WITH MAGNETIC DRIVE—THEY CAN GET THROUGH AND DESTROY THIS SATELLITE! NEVER...

AT THAT POINT THE SCREEN WENT BLANK, LEAVING MILLIONS OF VIEWERS WONDERING. WAS THIS ANOTHER OF THE MEKON'S TRICKS, OR HAD DAN DARE SENT THAT MESSAGE—AT THE COST OF HIS LIFE?

ER GENCY PING SITE

EAGLE

AND Boys' World

9 January 1965 Vol. 16 No. 2 — EVERY WEDNESDAY — **6d.**

DAN DARE
Pilot of the Future
in THE MUSHROOM

The Mekon had caused a great metallic mushroom to grow in the heart of London. Manned by Treens, this was able to freeze buildings beneath it and burn those at a distance. Although Dan and Digby were prisoners aboard the satellite, Dan managed to warn the spacefleet that had set out against it . . .

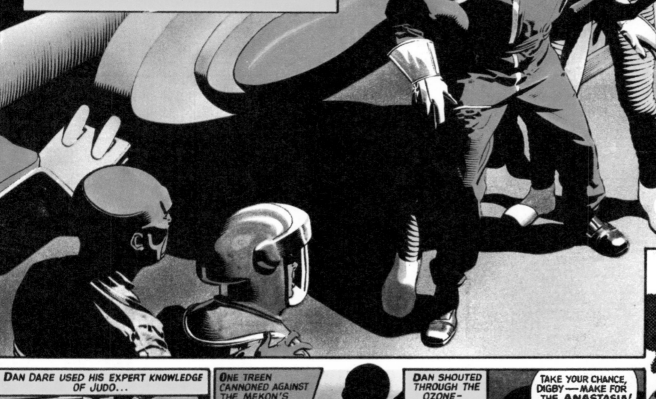

SILENCE THE EARTHMAN BEFORE HIS TONGUE DOES MORE DAMAGE TO OUR PLANS!

KEITH WATSON

KILL THE FAT EARTHMAN — HE MUST NOT ESCAPE!

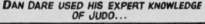

DAN DARE USED HIS EXPERT KNOWLEDGE OF JUDO...

AIIIEEE!

ONE TREEN CANNONED AGAINST THE MEKON'S POWER-FRINGED SAUCER...

AAAAH!

BLUNDERING FOOL!

DAN SHOUTED THROUGH THE OZONE-TAINTED AIR...

TAKE YOUR CHANCE, DIGBY — MAKE FOR THE ANASTASIA! THAT'S AN ORDER!

I HEAR AND OBEY, O MASTER!

EAGLE
AND Boys' World

16 January 1965   VOL. 16 No. 3   EVERY WEDNESDAY   6d.

DAN DARE
Pilot of the Future

in THE MUSHROOM

Dan Dare and Digby were held captive aboard the Mekon's satellite and had been forced to watch his systematic terrorization of London and other major cities. In order to destroy the control-centre of the huge, metallic mushroom that had grown in London, armed spaceships headed for the Mekon's satellite. But Dan warned them of the Mekon's destructive power . . .

LEAD SHIP TO SQUADRON— MISSION CANCELLED— RETURN TO EARTHSIDE ORBIT AT FOUR HUNDRED MILES AND AWAIT LANDING INSTRUCTIONS!

DAN DARE HAD WARNED THAT THE MEKON COULD DESTROY ALL SHIPS POWERED BY STANDARD SPACEFLEET IMPULSE MOTORS. BUT AT THAT MOMENT, THE CONTROL DUTY OFFICE HAD VISITORS...

WE UNDERSTAND THAT THERE IS A NEED FOR A SPACESHIP WITH MAGNETIC DRIVE !

WHY... ER...YES !

WE ARE VISITING EARTH ON A COURTESY CALL, BUT SINCE OUR SHIP HAS THE PROPULSIVE SYSTEM YOU REQUIRE, WE ARE VOLUNTEERING IT AND THE CREW INTO YOUR SERVICE!

THE VISITORS WERE THERONS FROM THE SOUTHERN HEMISPHERE OF VENUS, OLD ALLIES OF EARTH IN ITS STRUGGLE AGAINST THE MEKON, THE MAGNETIC SPACE DRIVE WAS THEIR INVENTION.

SHOULD YOU WISH TO PLACE ANY OF YOUR OWN MEN ABOARD...

THE DUTY OFFICER'S VIDEOPHONE BUZZED...

I'M PILOT CAPTAIN HANK HOGAN, SIR, A PERSONAL FRIEND OF COLONEL DARE, AND I'VE HAD EXPERIENCE WITH THERON MAGNETIC DRIVE. I WOULD LIKE TO VOLUNTEER FOR SERVICE ON ANY SHIP YOU MAY BE SENDING UP TO THAT SATELLITE!

HANK'S OFFER WAS ACCEPTED, AND WELL WITHIN THE HOUR, THE THERON VESSEL LEFT THE GROUND. MEANWHILE, COLONEL BANGER WAS MAKING OTHER PREPARATIONS FOR BREAKING THE MEKON'S ATTACK!

THIS TUNNEL WILL BE PACKED AND READY FOR BLASTING SOON, SIR !

GOOD! LET'S HOPE THE EXPLOSION UPROOTS THAT MUSHROOM!

MINUTES LATER, SIRENS WAILED ABOVE THE ALMOST EMPTY STREETS...

HURRY UP, THERE— WE HAVE LESS THAN TEN MINUTES TO GET CLEAR!

FINAL CHECKS WERE MADE ON THE EXPLOSIVES PACKED IN THE SUBWAYS AND TUNNELS THAT PASSED BENEATH THE AREA OF THE TERROR MUSHROOM...

FOR PITY'S SAKE, BERT, COME ON!

JUST CHECKING THAT THIS RADIO DETONATOR IS SET FOR THE CORRECT FREQUENCY!

THEN, AT PRECISELY THE PRE-ARRANGED SECOND, COLONEL BANGER JABBED HIS THUMB AT A HIGH-FREQUENCY DETONATOR TRIGGER.

NOW!

THE WHOLE CITY SHUDDERED, STREETS ERUPTED, THE GROUND SAGGED, AND THE ALIEN MUSHROOM LEANED CRAZILY TO ONE SIDE!

THE TREENS INSIDE IT ROLLED SCREAMING TO THE FLOOR!

EEEEEEH!

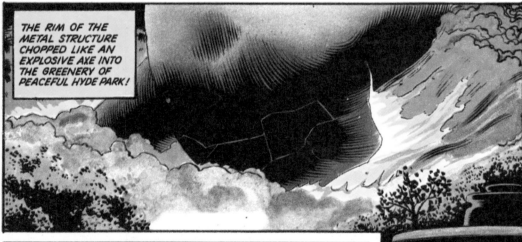

THE RIM OF THE METAL STRUCTURE CHOPPED LIKE AN EXPLOSIVE AXE INTO THE GREENERY OF PEACEFUL HYDE PARK!

WE'VE DONE IT! WE'VE BROUGHT IT DOWN!

HURRAY!

THREE CHEERS FOR, BANGER!

LONDON WAS SAVED, BUT THE EFFECT OF THE MUSHROOM'S COLLAPSE WAS FELT AS FAR AWAY AS THE SATELLITE WHICH CONTROLLED IT...

O MEKON— THE LONDON MUSHROOM IS DESTROYED.

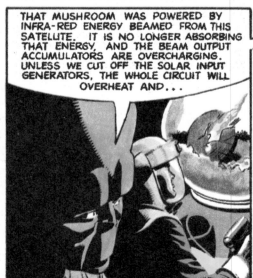

THAT MUSHROOM WAS POWERED BY INFRA-RED ENERGY BEAMED FROM THIS SATELLITE. IT IS NO LONGER ABSORBING THAT ENERGY, AND THE BEAM OUTPUT ACCUMULATORS ARE OVERCHARGING. UNLESS WE CUT OFF THE SOLAR INPUT GENERATORS, THE WHOLE CIRCUIT WILL OVERHEAT AND...

...BLOW UP! WE WILL ALL BE KILLED!

EAGLE
AND Boys' World

23 January 1965 Vol. 16 No. 4 · EVERY WEDNESDAY · 6d.

DAN DARE
Pilot of the Future

in THE MUSHROOM

Inside a satellite deep in space, Dan Dare held the Mekon and his evil Treens at gun-point. But an electronics panel exploded, and fire began spreading . . .

THERE ARE ESCAPE-CAPSULES, DARE! WE MUST TRY TO REACH THEM BEFORE WE ARE ALL BURNED ALIVE!

SEND THE TREENS ON AHEAD. YOU FOLLOW THEM, BUT I WARN YOU, MEKON, AT THE FIRST HINT OF TREACHERY, YOU WILL NOT LIVE TO ESCAPE!

DAN WATCHED CAUTIOUSLY AS, TWO BY TWO, THE TREENS ENTERED THE ESCAPE CAPSULES WHICH THEN FIRED THEM THROUGH THE SHELL OF THE DOOMED SATELLITE...

...AND INTO SPACE.

MORE ELECTRICAL CIRCUITS EXPLODED, AND THE SATELLITE WAS FILLED WITH A HUNDRED FIRES. EVERY TREEN HAD EJECTED TO SAFETY. NONE BUT DAN AND THE MEKON REMAINED ABOARD — OR SO THEY THOUGHT!

WHO'S THERE? WHO IS IT, MEKON?

I DO NOT KNOW, DARE! I WAS CERTAIN THAT WE WERE THE ONLY ONES LEFT INSIDE THIS SATELLITE!

BY HECK, AM I GLAD TO SEE YOU, SIR! I'VE BEEN REET LOST—THIS MEKON SATELLITE IS LIKE A MAZE!

DIGBY, OLD SPORT! I THOUGHT YOU WERE DEAD... I SAW YOU OUTSIDE, ON AN EXTERNAL VIDEO...

NOT ME, SIR! YOU SAW MY EMPTY SPACE-SUIT. I COULD NOT SQUEEZE INTO THE AIR-LOCK WITH IT ON, SO I TOOK IT OFF AND PUSHED IT IN FIRST. IT MUST HAVE BEEN A WASTE DISPOSAL LOCK, BECAUSE BEFORE I COULD ENTER IT CLOSED AUTOMATICALLY AND PUSHED MY SUIT OUT INTO SPACE!

SO THE MEKON SHOT AT NOTHING BUT YOUR EMPTY SPACE-SUIT!

I SUPPOSE SO, SIR, BUT WATCH THAT GREEN DEMON—HE'S UP TO SUMMAT!

THE MEKON WAS ABOUT TO TAKE THE LAST REMAINING ESCAPE CAPSULE!

FOOL, DARE, TO NEGLECT TO GUARD AN ENEMY WHILE YOU GREET A FRIEND!

DAN FIRED!

EEEEEK!

YOU HAVE DESTROYED YOUR ONLY MEANS OF REACHING SAFETY, DARE—NOT THAT YOU WILL BE CONCERNED WITH LIFE FOR MUCH LONGER...

AT THAT VERY INSTANT, A CABINET OF ELECTRONIC GEAR OVERHEATED TO EXPLOSION POINT...

WHERE'S THE MEKON, SIR? DID YOU GET HIM?

I CAN'T BE SURE, DIGBY! HE COULD BE LURKING ANY-WHERE IN THIS SMOKE, JUST WAITING TO KILL US!

DAN JIGGLED THE MOST PROMINENT LEVER. SUDDEN ACCELERATION KICKED HIS SEAT INTO HIS BACK. THERE WAS A ROLL AND A ROAR— AND THEN STARS WERE RUSHING PAST THE CANOPY...

OOOOO-PS! MY STOMACH!

I'M TRYING TO SLOW DOWN— AND FIND THE ANASTASIA!

DAN WAS STILL ERATICALLY ORBITING THE SATELLITE WHEN IT BLASTED APART, SHOOTING FIRE AND FLAME INTO SPACE!

BY GUM—THAT WAS CLOSE, SIR! WHAT WAS IT?

FOR A SECOND OR TWO, THE STARTLED EARTHMEN WATCHED THE GREEN BLOB OF HELLFIRE CURVE GENTLY AWAY INTO THE DISTANCE...

—IT WAS NO ORDINARY CHUNK OF DEBRIS, DIGBY! PROBABLY A PIECE OF THE POWER-PLANT...

...OR MAYBE THE MEKON!

HE CAN GO AS FAR AND AS FAST AS HE LIKES! FOR ME, I'M REET GLAD TO SEE OLD ANNIE AGAIN!

COME TO THINK OF IT, DIGBY, LOOKING AT THE ANASTASIA IS AS NEAR AS WE'LL GET TO IT!

WE CAN'T TRANSFER INTO THE ANASTASIA BECAUSE YOU HAVEN'T A SPACE-SUIT. WE CAN'T EVEN OPEN THIS COCK-PIT! WE'LL JUST HAVE TO SIT HERE—AND WAIT, AND HOPE!

DAN DARE KNEW THAT THE TINY ESCAPE CAPSULE WOULD NOT HOLD ENOUGH FUEL TO REACH EARTH!

THE CREW OF THE THERON SHIP DETECTED THE DESTRUCTION OF THE SATELLITE...

THERE IS A CLUSTER OF SMALL OBJECTS APPROACHING UNDER LOW POWER. THEY ARE PROBABLY THE SURVIVORS.

IS THERE ANY SIGN OF DAN DARE OR THE ANASTASIA?

CERTAINLY NOT AMONG THE APPROACHING CLUSTER!

THE THERON SHIP SLACKENED SPEED AS IT PREPARED TO PICK UP THE OCCUPANTS OF THE ESCAPE CAPSULES THAT HAD LEFT THE SATELLITE BEFORE THE EXPLOSION...

ALL THE CAPSULES CONTAIN TREENS. THERE IS NO SIGN OF COLONEL DARE OR DIGBY AMONG THEM!

PERHAPS THE ANASTASIA'S OUT OF ACTION—DAMAGED BY THE BLAST. IS THERE ANY OBJECT ON THE SCREEN THAT COULD BE IT?

SINCE THE SATELLITE EXPLODED, THIS SECTOR OF SPACE IS LITTERED WITH SUCH OBJECTS. IT WOULD BE AN IMPOSSIBLE TASK TO INVESTIGATE THEM ALL!

EAGLE
AND Boys' World

6 February 1965 Vol. 16 No. 6 — EVERY WEDNESDAY — **6d.**

DAN DARE
Pilot of the Future
in THE MUSHROOM

Dan Dare and Digby were in a small Treen escape capsule, but could not transfer to the *Anastasia* because Digby had no space-suit. The capsule did not have enough power to reach Earth . . .

SO BECAUSE I'VE NO SPACE-SUIT, WE'RE TRAPPED INSIDE THIS CAPSULE!

AFRAID SO, DIGBY! AND THERE'S VERY LITTLE CHANCE THAT A RESCUE SHIP WILL FIND US!

DAN DARE LOOKED AT THE ALIEN TREEN CONTROLS. SOME HE UNDERSTOOD, OTHERS HE DID NOT!

ONE OF THESE KNOBS MIGHT SEND OUT A SIGNAL—BUT I DARE NOT RISK CHOOSING THE WRONG ONE, AND PERHAPS DISCHARGING ALL OUR AIR!

IT'S A PITY THERE'S NO WAY OF TRIGGERING THE ANNIE'S DISTRESS SYSTEM!

YOU'VE HIT IT, DIGBY! THERE IS A WAY OF TRIGGERING THE ANASTASIA'S SIGNALS!

IT WAS A DESPERATE CHANCE...

IF WE CAN SMASH THE MAIN ELECTRONIC CONTROL SYSTEM, AN AUTOMATIC 'MAYDAY' WILL BE SENT OUT!

YOU MEAN WE'RE GOING TO DAMAGE THE ANASTASIA?

HOLD TIGHT, DIGBY!

AAAAH!

DAN HAD CAREFULLY CHOSEN THE ONE POINT OF COLLISION THAT WOULD FUSE ALL THE MAIN CIRCUITS ABOARD THE ANASTASIA. AUTOMATICALLY, IMPULSES TRIGGERED EMERGENCY DEVICES THAT FIRED FLARING DISTRESS ROCKETS OUT INTO SPACE...

A SPECIAL AUXILIARY TRANSMITTER EMITTED RADIO CALLS FOR HELP...

THERE'S A 'MAYDAY' SIGNAL FROM THE ANASTASIA! IT'S GIVING HER POSITION!

A THERON SPACESHIP, ALREADY RESCUING TREENS, WAS NEAREST...

WE ARE ABOUT TO MOVE TO ANOTHER POSITION TO INVESTIGATE CALL FROM ANASTASIA! ALL CREW ARE TO RETURN INBOARD AT ONCE!

HANK HOGAN, DAN DARE'S TEXAN FRIEND, WAS ABOARD THE THERON SHIP...

LET'S HOPE WE CAN GET TO THE COLONEL IN TIME!

MERCIFULLY, BOTH DAN AND DIGBY WERE SAFE WITHIN THE CAPSULE WHEN THE HUGE THERON SHIP MATCHED ORBIT ALONGSIDE...

THANKS—IT'S A GOOD JOB YOU CAME WHEN YOU DID! THE AIR WAS GETTING STUFFY INSIDE THAT CAPSULE!

IS THERE OWT YOU CAN DO FOR THE OLD ANNIE?

SURE— THEY'RE HITCHING HER ALONGSIDE FOR A TOW HOME!

HOW'S LONDON, HANK? THINGS WERE NOT TOO HAPPY WHEN I LEFT!

ACCORDING TO THE LAST REPORT, EVERYTHING'S FINE. THEY'VE CLEARED UP A LOT OF THE MESS ALREADY. COLONEL BANGER MADE THE BANG OF HIS LIFE WHEN HE BLEW UP THE MEKON'S MUSHROOM!

NO ONE KNOWS WHAT THE THING WAS MADE OF, BUT AT THE RATE IT'S GOING NOW, THAT MUSHROOM WILL BURN FOR ANOTHER WEEK!

IN FACT, THE GUTTED MUSHROOM BECAME SOMETHING OF A TOURIST ATTRACTION...

HOT MUSHROOM PIES

YOU'RE NOT ENJOYING YOUR MUSHROOM PIE, DIGBY!

NAY, SIR—AND FROM NOW ON MUSHROOMS WILL DO NOWT BUT REMIND ME O' SUMMAT UNPLEASANT...

...THE MEKON!

THE MEKON, INDEED! I WONDER IF HE DID ESCAPE FROM THAT SATELLITE... I WONDER IF HE IS DEAD OR ALIVE!

EAGLE
AND Boys' World

13 February 1965   VOL. 16 No. 7   EVERY WEDNESDAY   6d.

DAN DARE
Pilot of the Future
in THE MOONSLEEPERS

Escorted by armed patrols, the alien Xel was flown from a Spacefleet ship far out in space. The law of the twenty-first century was merciful to the repentant criminal, but Xel had cursed the Earth and all men on it. He raved only of destruction and killing and rule by terror!

KEITH WATSON

HIS OWN SAVAGE WORDS HAD COMPELLED THE LAW TO SENTENCE HIM TO A FATE WORSE THAN THAT SUFFERED BY A MUTINEER PIRATE MAROONED ON A REMOTE SOUTH SEA ISLAND...

AND SO THE VICIOUS ALIEN WAS TRANSPORTED TO A DERELICT SPACE STATION, FAR FROM THE HUMAN RACE HE HAD THREATENED TO DESTROY...

"THERE ARE RATIONS HERE FOR TWO YEARS, BUT A RELIEF SHIP WILL CALL ONCE EVERY ELEVEN MONTHS WITH SUPPLIES AND OTHER ESSENTIALS. AT LEAST YOU WILL NOT STARVE!"

THE MEN AND THE GUNS WENT AWAY. THE AIR-LOCK HISSED INTO SILENCE. XEL WOULD SEE NO LIVING CREATURE FOR ALMOST A YEAR. HE KICKED HIS SPACE TOMB WITH A SAVAGE OUTBURST...

GNAAAH!

RAGE CONGEALED INTO FRENZIED EFFORTS TO ESCAPE—DESPERATELY, ANGRILY, HE SOUGHT THE MATERIALS FOR A SMALL SPACE CAPSULE ...

BUT THE PRISON SATELLITE HAD BEEN EXPERTLY DENUDED OF EVERY MECHANICAL DEVICE EXCEPT THOSE THAT PROVIDED ESSENTIAL LIGHT AND AIR. THE ALIEN FLAMED INTO A TERRIBLE FURY!

WHAT USE WILL MY CAPSULE BE WITHOUT AN ENGINE—I AM JUST MAKING MYSELF A SMALLER PRISON!

XEL WAS OFFERED THE CHANCE TO LIVE HERE IN PEACE, BUT HE REFUSED IT. HE BROUGHT EXILE UPON HIMSELF!

EEE—AT LEAST THEY'RE LAYING ON A BIG DO FOR SIR HUBERT WHEN HE COMES BACK FROM VISITING PRESIDENT KALON OF THE THERONS.

BACK TO HELIPORT

HE'S DUE IN A FEW HOURS—JUST IN TIME TO CELEBRATE THE PUBLICATION OF HIS MEMOIRS!

THE ALIEN WAS FORGOTTEN. ONE DAY, THE SIGHT OF THE TIME-SHIP TEMPUS FRANGIT REMINDED DAN DARE AND HIS BATMAN DIGBY OF HIM ...

THEY'LL SOON HAVE THE MODIFICATIONS FINISHED ON THE TEMPUS FRANGIT! XEL CAME ON IT, AS A STOWAWAY, MAYBE, BUT IT'S A SHAME WE COULDN'T USE IT TO TAKE HIM BACK WHERE HE BELONGS!

OUT OF THE QUESTION, DIG! TIME TRAVELLING IS TOO EXPENSIVE TO USE EVEN FOR GOOD DEEDS. EVEN IF WE DID GET HIM BACK TO HIS OWN TIME, THE TEMPUS FRANGIT WOULD NOT CARRY ENOUGH FUEL TO LOCATE STOL, HIS HOME WORLD!

ADVANCE PUBLICITY HAS ALREADY CREATED A TERRIFIC AMOUNT OF INTEREST!

BY GUM, I WONDER IF HE'LL HAVE ANYTHING TO SAY ABOUT US!

THE PARTING GUEST

MEMOIRS OF SIR HUBERT GUEST G.C.B. O.M. C.H. O.W. D.S.O. D.F.C.

MEMORIES FLASHED ACROSS DAN'S MIND, OF THE FIRST MISSION TO VENUS, LED BY SIR HUBERT GUEST, AND OF MANY OTHER ADVENTURES BEFORE THE OLD WARRIOR RETIRED. SUDDENLY...

COLONEL DARE REPORT TO CONTROL—URGENT—COLONEL DARE TO REPORT TO CONTROL!

SERIOUS FACES AND SERIOUS NEWS AWAITED DAN DARE ...

CONTACT HAS BEEN LOST WITH THE THERON SHIP BRINGING SIR HUBERT! THE WORST IS FEARED — AND I HAVE ALREADY INITIATED A FULL-SCALE SEARCH AND RESCUE OPERATION!

SIR HUBERT! BUT THAT SORT OF DISASTER JUST DOESN'T HAPPEN TO MEN LIKE HIM!

SIR HUBERT MAY STILL BE UP THERE WAITING FOR HELP! AND IN THE ANASTASIA WE CAN GET TO HIM FASTER THAN ANYONE!

AYE, SIR— BUT WE COULD BE TOO LATE ALREADY!

THESE THERONS DID NOT DIE BECAUSE OF ANY SPACESHIP DISASTER! THEY HAVE BEEN SHOT!

THESE ARE SIR HUBERT'S PERSONAL PAPERS!

SO HE MUST HAVE BEEN HERE! BUT WHO DID THE SHOOTING—AND WHERE DID SIR HUBERT GO?

THE ANSWER TO DAN'S URGENT QUESTION COULD BE FOUND INSIDE THE METEOR-POCKED WALLS OF XEL'S PRISON-SATELLITE...

NO LONGER WAS THE SATELLITE'S EVIL INMATE IN SOLITARY CONFINEMENT—HE HAD GUESTS!

WHY SHOULD I TRUST YOU, MEKON?

BECAUSE I AM GIVING YOU A SPACESHIP CAPTURED FROM VENUS, A HOSTAGE FROM EARTH AND THE OPPORTUNITY TO ESCAPE TO ANYWHERE YOU WISH...

I WANT POWER, MEKON! I WANT THE POWER TO RULE, TO DESTROY, TO WAGE WAR, TO CONQUER, TO MAKE WHOLE EMPIRES TREMBLE AT MY WORD! FIRST, I WILL NEED AN ARMY!

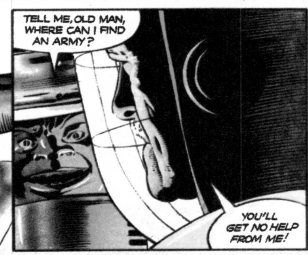

TELL ME, OLD MAN, WHERE CAN I FIND AN ARMY?

YOU'LL GET NO HELP FROM ME!

A STRANGE POWER EMANATING FROM THE EERILY-GLOWING TIPS OF XEL'S HELMET BEGAN TO DISSOLVE EVEN SIR HUBERT'S IRON WILL-POWER...

TRY TRITON, THE LARGEST MOON OF NEPTUNE, THE EIGHTH PLANET FROM THE SUN.

THERON ASTRONOMERS HAVE DETECTED SIGNS OF LIFE THERE!

HOURLY, THE SEARCH FOR THE LOST SPACE MARSHAL WIDENED...

AS TIME DRAGGED FRUITLESSLY BY, EVEN THE UNLIKELY DERELICT SPACE STATION WAS BROUGHT WITHIN THE WIDENED SCOPE OF THE SEARCH...

DO YOU THINK SIR HUBERT COULD HAVE REACHED THAT?

IT'S A FEEBLE HOPE, DIGBY, BUT IT WILL DO NO HARM TO SEE!

THE ANASTASIA'S MAGNETIC MOORING LINES HUGGED HER CLOSE AGAINST THE HUB OF THE OLD SPACE STATION, AND HER TWO-MAN CREW JETTED TOWARDS THE SEALED AIR-LOCK...

DANGER NO UNAUTHORISED ENTRY

ATTENTION DEFENSE D'ENTRER

IT MAKES A CHANGE FROM 'WELCOME' ON THE DOORMAT! I WONDER WHAT WE WILL FIND INSIDE!

EAGLE
AND Boys' World

27 February 1965 Vol. 16 No. 9.

EVERY WEDNESDAY 6d.

WARNING DANGEROUS ALIEN

DAN DARE
Pilot of the Future
in THE MOONSLEEPERS

Dan Dare was about to search a derelict satellite for Sir Hubert Guest, retired Spacefleet Controller, who was aboard a Theron spaceship that had vanished. The satellite was the prison to which the vicious alien Xel had been condemned to perpetual solitary confinement . . .

KEEP ALERT, DIGBY! THIS IS XEL'S PRISON. HE MAY BE WAITING TO JUMP ON US THE MOMENT WE STEP INSIDE!

BUT THE SATELLITE WAS EMPTY . . .

THERE'S NO ONE HERE! XEL'S GONE!

BE CAREFUL — HE MAY BE WAITING FOR US AT THE NEXT INTERSECTION!

DIGBY! LOOK AT THIS!

WHAT IS IT, SIR?

HE HAS BEEN BUILDING HIMSELF AN ESCAPE CRAFT!

THEN HE HAS GONE WITHOUT IT — OR HE IS STILL HERE, WAITING HIS CHANCE TO GET US!

EAGLE
AND Boys' World
6 March 1965   VOL. 16 No.10   EVERY WEDNESDAY   6d.

DAN DARE
Pilot of the Future
in THE MOONSLEEPERS

Xel, a vicious, power-hungry alien, had taken Sir Hubert Guest as a hostage to the moon of Neptune, known as Triton. They entered a cold, long-dead city, and Sir Hubert was bowled over by a sudden bolt of white light – one of many similar fireballs that soon eased their play as the uncontrolled machinery that discharged them drained of surplus electrical power . . .

KEITH WATSON

XEL CROUCHED IN A SNOWY STREET. HIS CUNNING EYES WATCHED THE STRANGE LIGHTS...

THE CITY SKY QUIETENED AFTER A FEW MINUTES...

DEAD OR NEARLY DEAD! IT MAKES NO DIFFERENCE – HE WILL BE NO MORE USE TO ME! I CAN SPARE NO TIME FOR NURSING WEAKLINGS!

THE ALIEN STRODE AWAY...

THE EARTHMAN REMAINED, SPRAWLED IN THE ICE, HIS FACEPLATE ALREADY FROSTING IN THE SUB-ZERO TEMPERATURE.

AND BY CRUEL COINCIDENCE, THE VETERAN SPACE-MAN'S RECORD FILE AT EARTH H.Q. WAS AT THAT MOMENT OFFICIALLY CLOSED...

SIR. HUBERT GASCOIGNE GUEST
K.C.B., O.M., O.U.N., D.S.O., D.F.C.

MISSING PRESUMED DEAD

THE PAPER RECORDS OF THE HERO'S LIFE WERE MICRO-FILMED, THEN DESTROYED...

IS THAT REALLY ALL THAT REMAINS OF SIR HUBERT'S LIFE — SEVEN SPOOLS OF MICRO-FILM!

SPACE-FLEE RECORDS

I'D LIKE TO BELIEVE THAT HE'S STILL ALIVE. AFTER ALL, HE WAS AS TOUGH AS THEY COME!

BUT HE HAS BEEN AWAY TOO LONG, THERE HAS BEEN NO SOUND, NO CLUE, NO SIGNAL, NOT EVEN A HINT THAT HE SURVIVED THE THERON SHIP DISASTER!

AYE, BUT WE COULD JUST SAY THAT HE DISAPPEARED AT THE TIME OF THE DISASTER, NOW IF THE MEKON WERE ALIVE, I'D SAY...

MAYBE THE MEKON IS STILL ALIVE! NO ONE PROVED HIS DEATH IN THAT SATELLITE. THERE'S ALSO XEL'S ESCAPE FROM HIS ESCAPE-PROOF PRISON! MYSTERIES ALL ALONG THE LINE!

BUT IF SIR HUBERT WERE DEAD, HE HAD NO INTENTION OF LYING DOWN...

MUST KEEP GOING — OOH, MY HEAD! ACHE ALL OVER — WHAT'S XEL DOING?

XEL WAS A HUNDRED YARDS AWAY, WATCHING A FAN BLOWING STEAM OUT OF A VENT...

SMOKE OR STEAM — THAT CAN MEAN ONLY ONE THING — HEAT! AND ON THIS FREEZING MOON, HEAT MUST MEAN LIFE! I AM AT THE END OF MY SEARCH!

XEL FOUND A DOOR THROUGH THAT WALL, AND THRUST IT OPEN...

MUST KEEP AFTER XEL — MUST SEE WHAT HE DOES HERE...

SIR HUBERT FOLLOWED THE STRUTTING ALIEN INTO THE STRANGE BUILDING THAT PROMISED LIFE. HE FELT HIS WAY DOWN THE RAMP AND PEERED CAUTIOUSLY AROUND THE FIRST CORNER

GREAT GALLOPING GANYMEDE!

SOMEHOW, I MUST GET BACK TO EARTH AND WARN THE AUTHORITIES! THEY MUST BE ALERTED AT ALL COSTS!

SUMMONING EVERY FEEBLE SHRED OF STRENGTH, THE OLD WARRIOR HASTENED OUT OF THE TOWN, FEARFULLY AWARE THAT AT ANY TIME XEL COULD DISCOVER HIS TRACKS...

A TWELVE-HOUR JOURNEY TO THE SPACESHIP — AND EVEN A MOMENT'S REST MIGHT BE FATAL. I'M ALREADY TIRED — SO TIRED!

SIR HUBERT MEANT TO SURVIVE BY SAVING HIS FUEL, FOOD, AIR AND WATER...

IF I CAN LAST OUT UNTIL I REACH EARTH, I CAN WARN THE AUTHORITIES ABOUT XEL AND THE MEKON. DARE COULD HANDLE THE SITUATION ON TRITON—IF ONLY I HAVE ENOUGH SUPPLIES!

FOOD SUPPLIES

...BUT THERE WAS TOO LITTLE OF EVERYTHING!

XEL WAS UNCONCERNED. HE RETURNED TO THE CITY OF TRITON...

THIS WILL BE THE FOUNDATION OF MY EMPIRE! HERE IS INDUSTRY TO BUILD MACHINES AND WEAPONS...

INSIDE ONE OF THE GREAT BUILDINGS...

AND HERE IS A CIVILIZED RACE TO BECOME MY SERVANTS AND WARRIORS!

WITHOUT WARNING, XEL POUNCED SAVAGELY UPON ONE OF THE PLACID BEINGS!

FOOD, DRINK, HEAT. EVERYTHING IS PROVIDED BY MACHINE, SO THEY HAVE TO DO NOTHING! HAH—BUT SOON THEY WILL HAVE TO WORK!

GOOD! THEY SHOW FEAR! THEN I SHALL RULE THEM BY FEAR!

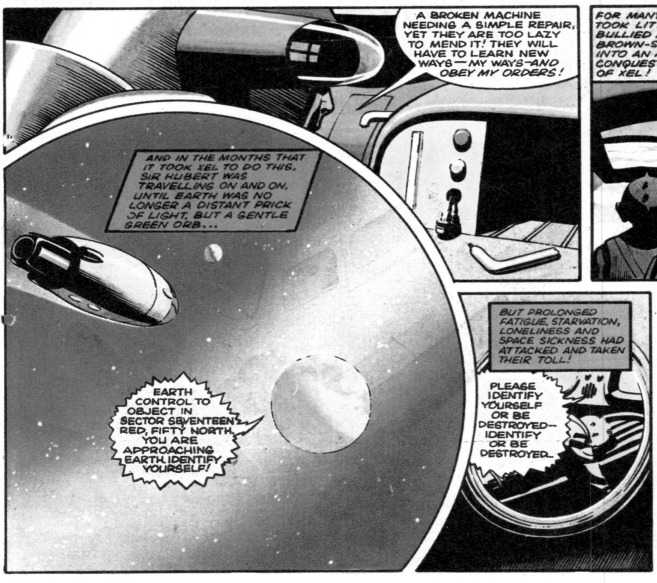

A BROKEN MACHINE NEEDING A SIMPLE REPAIR, YET THEY ARE TOO LAZY TO MEND IT! THEY WILL HAVE TO LEARN NEW WAYS—MY WAYS—AND OBEY MY ORDERS!

AND IN THE MONTHS THAT IT TOOK XEL TO DO THIS, SIR HUBERT WAS TRAVELLING ON AND ON, UNTIL EARTH WAS NO LONGER A DISTANT PRICK OF LIGHT, BUT A GENTLE GREEN ORB...

EARTH CONTROL TO OBJECT IN SECTOR SEVENTEEN RED, FIFTY NORTH. YOU ARE APPROACHING EARTH. IDENTIFY YOURSELF!

FOR MANY WEEKS, THE ALIEN TOOK LITTLE REST WHILE HE BULLIED AND DRILLED THE BROWN-SKINNED TRITONS INTO AN ARMY—AN ARMY OF CONQUEST IN THE NAME OF XEL!

BUT PROLONGED FATIGUE, STARVATION, LONELINESS AND SPACE SICKNESS HAD ATTACKED AND TAKEN THEIR TOLL!

PLEASE IDENTIFY YOURSELF OR BE DESTROYED—IDENTIFY OR BE DESTROYED.

IN EARTH CONTROL...

WHAT DO WE DO, COLONEL DARE—ASSUME THAT IT'S HOSTILE AND SEND AN ANTI-MISSILE TO KILL IT?

IF IT WERE FRIENDLY IT WOULD SEND A SIGNAL OF SOME KIND—ALERT THE MISSILE CREWS!

THERE'S SOMEONE IN HERE!

IS HE STILL ALIVE?

SIR HUBERT!

SORRY ABOUT THAT LANDING—MESSY! MUST TELL YOU...

NEVER MIND NOW, SIR HUBERT—YOU NEED MEDICAL ATTENTION!

EAGER, HELPFUL HANDS LIFTED THE LIMP TRAVELLER FROM WHAT HAD SO NEARLY BECOME HIS TOMB IN SPACE...

SAW THE MEKON—AND XEL—ON TRITON! STOP THEM, DAN—YOU MUST STOP... UUUH!

SIR HUBERT COLLAPSED, HIS JAW SAGGED AND HIS EYES CLOSED...

BY GUM! DO YOU REALLY THINK HE SAW THEM—XEL, AND THE MEKON...?

OR WERE THEY JUST DREAMS, HALLUCINATIONS BROUGHT ON BY HUNGER AND SUFFERING?

A CONFERENCE WAS HELD TO DISCUSS THIS QUESTION...

SIR HUBERT HAS BEEN IN A COMA FOR THREE DAYS AND HE MAY NEVER RECOVER. HOW MUCH IMPORTANCE SHOULD WE PLACE UPON WORDS GASPED OUT BY A MAN AS ILL AS SIR HUBERT!

TESTS SHOW THAT THE CAPSULE WAS EXPOSED, IN SPACE, FOR SEVERAL WEEKS TO UNSHIELDED COSMIC RADIATIONS. BUT AT MOST THIS ONLY ACCOUNTS FOR THREE QUARTERS OF THE TIME SINCE THE THERON SHIP VANISHED!

THEN IT IS POSSIBLE THAT SIR HUBERT WENT, OR WAS TAKEN, TO TRITON IN THE THERON SHIP. BUT THE RETURN JOURNEY IN SUCH A CAPSULE IS IMPOSSIBLE!

SIR HUBERT MADE IT POSSIBLE! I BELIEVE HE ENDURED THOSE NIGHTMARE WEEKS OF SUFFERING TO WARN US, THEREFORE I REQUEST AUTHORITY TO VISIT TRITON IN THE ANASTASIA!

ANASTASIA

THE ANASTASIA WAS THE ONLY SHIP ON EARTH THAT POSSESSED THE THERON-DESIGNED MAGNETIC MOTORS THAT COULD TAKE IT AS FAR AS NEPTUNE'S MOONS. DAN'S REQUEST WAS FINALLY GRANTED...

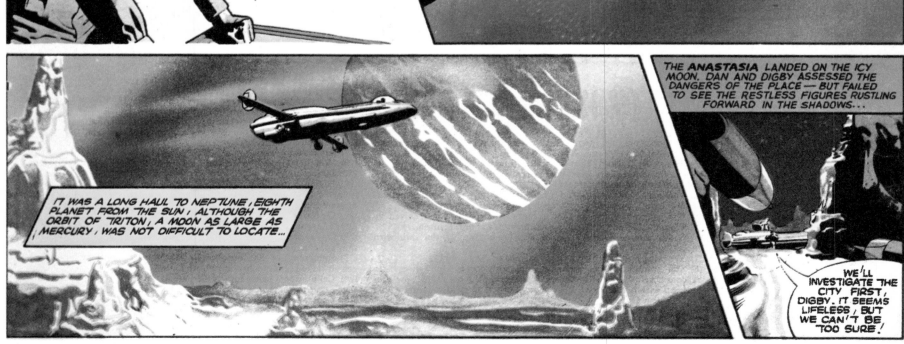

IT WAS A LONG HAUL TO NEPTUNE, EIGHTH PLANET FROM THE SUN; ALTHOUGH THE ORBIT OF TRITON, A MOON AS LARGE AS MERCURY, WAS NOT DIFFICULT TO LOCATE...

THE ANASTASIA LANDED ON THE ICY MOON. DAN AND DIGBY ASSESSED THE DANGERS OF THE PLACE—BUT FAILED TO SEE THE RESTLESS FIGURES RUSTLING FORWARD IN THE SHADOWS...

WE'LL INVESTIGATE THE CITY FIRST, DIGBY. IT SEEMS LIFELESS, BUT WE CAN'T BE TOO SURE!

EAGLE
AND Boys' World

27 March 1965   Vol. 16 No. 13

EVERY WEDNESDAY   6d.

DAN DARE
Pilot of the Future

in THE MOONSLEEPERS

Dan Dare, with Digby, had arrived on Triton, one of Neptune's moons, rightly suspecting that Xel was already there planning trouble for the Earth. A party of Tritons saw the *Anastasia* arrive . . .

HERE COME THE LOCALS—AND THEY'RE NOT VERY FRIENDLY!

PICK YOUR TARGETS, DIGBY!

BY GUM, SIR, THERE'S PLENTY TO PICK FROM!

THE TRITONS SWARMED SAVAGELY ACROSS THE POWDERED ICE...

THE TRITONS' MARKSMANSHIP WAS ERRATIC—AND THE TWO EARTHMEN SOON SHOT MOST OF THEM DOWN...

XEL HAD TAUGHT THE TRITONS HOW TO FIGHT, BUT HE HAD NOT TAUGHT THEM TO EXPECT CASUALTIES!

LOOK AT THAT, SIR! THEY'RE RUNNING!

COME ON, THEN. LET'S SEE WHERE THEY ARE RUNNING TO!

IT WAS A LONG CHASE, WITH THE MEN UNABLE TO CLOSE WITH THE FLEEING TRITONS...

WE'LL LEARN NOTHING IF WE STAY UP HERE—AND WE'VE COME MILLIONS OF MILES TO FIND XEL. THAT CITY IS WHERE WE MAY FIND HIM— COME ON!

SHALL WE FOLLOW THEM ALL THE WAY?

BUT THE VOYAGERS FROM HALFWAY ACROSS THE SOLAR SYSTEM FOUND THE CITY OF TRITON DESERTED...

BY GUM, THIS IS A CITY OF THE DEAD, IF EVER THERE WAS ONE!

BE CAREFUL— OR IT MAY TURN OUT TO BE AN AMBUSH!

BUT FINDING NO LIFE OUTSIDE, DAN FINALLY VENTURED INTO ONE OF THE LARGER BUILDINGS...

THERE THEY ARE!

EEEE, HECK! A WHOLE NESTFUL!

PANIC LASHED THE ROOM LIKE AN ICY GALE!

THEN THERE CAME AN IMPERIOUS COMMAND!

STOP! I, XEL, THE ONE WHO IS OBEYED, COMMAND YOU! STOP— AND WATCH THESE EARTHMEN DIE!

THE METAL LASH WAS ELECTRICALLY CHARGED— BUT THE VOLTS COULD NOT BITE THROUGH THE HEAVY INSULATION OF DAN'S SPACE GLOVE!

DROPPING HIS GUN, DAN GRASPED THE GLISTENING LASH AND JERKED WITH ALL HIS STRENGTH...

GNAA-AAAA-AH!

THE ALIEN SHATTERED THE GLOWING STRUCTURE, AND RELEASED A SEARING BLAST OF FLAME!

UUUH!

EAGLE
AND Boys' World
3 April 1965   VOL. 16 No. 14   EVERY WEDNESDAY   **6d.**

DAN DARE
Pilot of the Future
in THE MOONSLEEPERS

Dan Dare and Digby had arrived on Triton, where they believed Xel was amassing an armada to invade Earth. So far, they had found a semi-derelict city and a few weak natives – the Tritons. Suddenly, Xel raged threateningly on to the scene – exploding a stove and setting a building on fire . . .

THIS BUILDING IS BURNING LIKE PAPER!

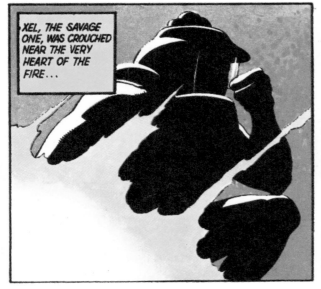

XEL, THE SAVAGE ONE, WAS CROUCHED NEAR THE VERY HEART OF THE FIRE . . .

THE TRITONS HAD ALREADY FLED BY A DOZEN EXITS INTO THE ICY SEMI-NIGHT OF TRITON . . .

BY GUM, WHAT A BLAZE—AND XEL IS STILL INSIDE!

AND HIS FRIENDS THE TRITONS ARE DOING NOTHING!

EAGLE
AND Boys' World

10 April 1965   Vol. 16 No. 15

EVERY WEDNESDAY   6d.

15th ANNIVERSARY SPECIAL

DAN DARE
Pilot of the Future
in THE MOONSLEEPERS

Dan Dare and Digby had followed the vicious alien Xel to Triton. It was from this moon of Neptune that Xel planned to attack Earth . . .

XEL'S INVASION ARMADA—ALL READY TO ATTACK EARTH!

KEITH WATSON

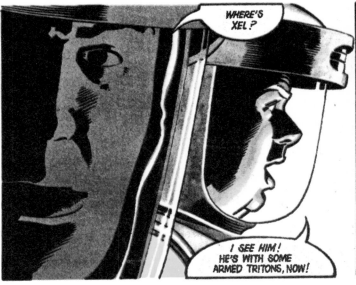

WHERE'S XEL?

I SEE HIM! HE'S WITH SOME ARMED TRITONS, NOW!

XEL WAS JUST TAKING OFF IN ONE OF HIS BUBBLE CRAFT...

WHAT'S UP? WHAT'S THE RUSH?

I'VE JUST REALIZED THAT XEL ISN'T BOTHERED WITH US—BECAUSE NOW HE'S AFTER THE ANASTASIA! WE MUST STOP HIM!

DAN RUSHED TO THE NEAREST OF XEL'S BUBBLE CRAFT...

DAN DARE AND DIGBY HAD LEARNED ABOUT THE STRANGE WORKINGS OF XEL'S BUBBLE CRAFT IN AN EARLIER ENCOUNTER WITH THE ALIEN...

COME ON, DIGBY! IF XEL GETS TO THE ANASTASIA FIRST, THERE WILL BE NOTHING WE CAN DO TO STOP HIM ATTACKING EARTH!

THE WEIRD, FLAME-POWERED CRAFT SKIMMED THE BLEAK TRITON LANDSCAPE...

BUT...

WE'RE BEING FOLLOWED! WHO ARE THEY...?

NOT OUR PEOPLE, O GREAT ONE! THEY ARE STRANGERS!

XEL HAULED HIS CRAFT BACK IN A MAGNIFICENT LOOP...

...AND A FLAME-BOLT SKEWERED THE CANOPY OF DAN'S MACHINE WITH DEADLY PRECISION...

THERE WAS NO SUCH WORD AS MERCY IN THE ALIEN'S BRUTAL LANGUAGE...

O XEL, WHO IS OBEYED, A MESSAGE FROM OUR GREEN ALLY IS BEING RECEIVED BY HEADQUARTERS!

TELL THEM TO RELAY IT TO ME HERE!

XEL TURNED FROM HIS CAPTIVES TO THE VIDEO IN HIS BUBBLE CRAFT. THEN A PALLID, INDISTINCT IMAGE APPEARED—OF MANKIND'S ARCH ENEMY, THE MEKON!

IT'S OLD MELON-HEAD HIMSELF! SO HE IS IN CAHOOTS WITH XEL, AFTER ALL!

XEL, IS YOUR SPACE-FLEET FUELLED AND ARMED? IS YOUR ARMY TRAINED? ARE ALL OBSTACLES CLEARED FROM YOUR PATH OF AGGRESSION?

ALL OF THEM!

THEN LISTEN AS I DESCRIBE THE PLAN BY WHICH WE SHALL SHATTER EARTH'S DEFENCE FORCES FOR EVER!

EAGLE

AND Boys' World

17 April 1965   VOL. 16 No. 16   EVERY WEDNESDAY   6d.

DAN DARE
Pilot of the Future
in THE MOONSLEEPERS

Xel, a ruthless alien, had amassed an armada on Triton and had allied with the sinister Mekon to attack the Earth. Dan Dare and Digby were on Triton, but they had been captured by Xel and the Tritons who served him . . .

ALL THE EARTH SHALL BE MINE — AND DEATH SHALL BE THE REWARD FOR ALL WHO DARE TO OPPOSE ME!

THE MEKON'S PLAN IS THAT WE KEEP EARTH DEFENCES AND THEIR THERON FRIENDS ON VENUS DIVIDED, BY MAKING TWO ATTACKS AT ONCE. THE MEKON WILL ATTACK VENUS AND I SHALL ATTACK EARTH . . .

BUT THE FIRST EARTHMAN I SHALL KILL WILL BE . . . AAAH!

DAN HELPED DIGBY TEAR FREE FROM HIS ESCORT — THEN THE EARTHMEN RAN . . .

MAKE FOR THE ANNIE, DIGBY! IT'S OUR ONLY HOPE!

AYE, AND A DISTANT ONE!

XEL SQUINTED HIS YELLOW, HATE-LIT EYES AND FIRED AT THE FUGITIVES . . .

AAAAH!

DAN DARE AND DIGBY FELL, AND THE ICY SURFACE OF THE GROUND FELL WITH THEM, HITTING AND BEATING THEM AS IT WENT...

THERE ARE MANY SUCH HIDDEN CHASMS AS THIS ON THE PLAINS OF TRITON. MOST OF THEM ARE HUNDREDS OF FEET DEEP!

THEN WE CAN HAPPILY ASSUME THAT THE EARTHMEN ARE DEAD!

XEL STALKED AROUND THE END OF THE CREVASSE OF DEATH TO CLAIM HIS PRIZE— DAN DARE'S OWN SPACESHIP, *ANASTASIA!*

THIS WILL BE THE FLAGSHIP OF MY BATTLE FLEET! I SHALL LEAD THE ATTACK ON EARTH— IN EARTH'S MOST FAMOUS SPACESHIP!

BUT... DIGBY! DIGBY— CAN YOU HEAR ME?

DAN THRUST ASIDE A BOULDER TO FREE HIMSELF...

...AND UNWITTINGLY CAUSED A SECONDARY AVALANCHE...

HEY! SINCE WHEN HAS IT BEEN FRIENDLY TO CHUCK ROCKS AT FOLKS!

DIGBY! THANK GOODNESS YOU'RE ALL RIGHT!

AS THEY CLAWED THEIR WAY UPWARDS, DAN REALIZED THAT ONLY THE LIGHT PULL OF GRAVITY EXERTED BY THE MOON TRITON HAD SAVED THEM FROM DEATH IN THEIR FALL. HE WAS ALSO AWARE OF THE NEED FOR EXTREME URGENCY!

CAN'T WE REST A BIT, SIR? I'M FAIR WHACKED!

WE'RE IN A RACE AGAINST TIME, DIGBY. IF WE LOSE A MINUTE — WE MAY LOSE THE WORLD!

FOR, INDEED, XEL HAD ALREADY GIVEN THE FIRST ORDERS FOR HIS INTENDED RUTHLESS ATTACK ON EARTH!

EAGLE
AND Boys' World

24 April 1965   Vol. 16 No. 17   EVERY WEDNESDAY   6d.

DAN DARE
Pilot of the Future
in THE MOONSLEEPERS

Xel, a ruthless alien, was planning to invade Earth from Triton, a moon of Neptune. He had captured Dan Dare's famous spaceship *Anastasia*, and intended to use it to lead his powerful armada . . .

KEITH WATSON

SO MUCH FOR THE PRIDE OF EARTH'S SPACEFLEET!

XEL HAD LEFT DAN DARE AND DIGBY FOR DEAD AT THE BOTTOM OF AN ICE CREVASSE, BUT THEY HAD SURVIVED THE LONG FALL BECAUSE TRITON'S GRAVITY WAS TOO WEAK TO KILL THEM . . .

BY GUM— WEAK GRAVITY OR NOT, THAT WERE A STIFF CLIMB UP!

THERE'S NO TIME FOR PANTING AND COMPLAINING— EVERY SECOND WE WASTE GETTING BACK TO THE CITY MAY BE VITAL!

AYE, SIR— BUT XEL FLEW TO THE CITY IN OUR ANASTASIA!

ALL THE MORE REASON FOR OUR HURRY— BEFORE HE USES IT TO FLY ON TO EARTH!

BUT XEL'S TRITON ARMY WAS ALREADY BOARDING HIS ARMADA!

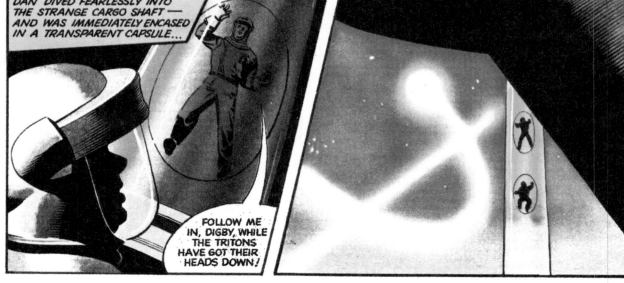

INSIDE THE DARK, VIBRATING HOLD OF A TRITON SHIP...

BY HECK, SIR! I'M SUFFOCATING— THESE THINGS MUST BE AIR— TIGHT AND HEAT— PROOF!

PROBABLY SHOCK-PROOF, TOO!

JUDGING BY THE SUSTAINED ENGINE ROAR, WE'VE TAKEN OFF— AND IF THERE WAS THE NORMAL ACCELERATION NEEDED FOR TAKE-OFF, WE'D HAVE BROKEN OUR NECKS IN THE POSITION WE'RE IN — UNLESS SOMETHING SCREENED US FROM THE G-FORCES!

YET FOR ALL THE TRANSPARENT CASING'S PROPERTIES, IT YIELDED TO DAN'S KNIFE...

AS SOON AS YOU'VE RECOVERED, DIGBY, WE'VE GOT SOME EXPLORING TO DO! THE MORE WE CAN LEARN ABOUT THIS SHIP BEFORE WE'RE DISCOVERED, THE BETTER!

AYE, SIR!

THE CHANCES ARE THAT THE CREW'S QUARTERS AND CONTROL DECK ARE UP HERE...

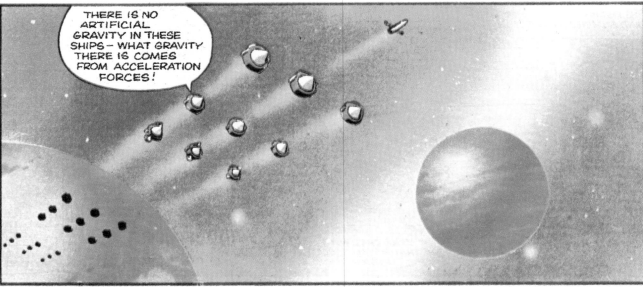

THERE IS NO ARTIFICIAL GRAVITY IN THESE SHIPS — WHAT GRAVITY THERE IS COMES FROM ACCELERATION FORCES!

HERE ARE THE CREW!

AND BUSY WITH THEIR FAVOURITE OCCUPATION— SLEEPING!

THIS SITUATION SUITED DAN. HE HAD NO WISH TO BE SEEN UNTIL HE HAD LEARNED A LOT MORE ABOUT THE SHIP...

EVEN THE DUTY CONTROL OFFICER IS DOZING!

LET'S TAKE A LOOK AT THE CONTROLS!

BUT AS DIGBY MOVED ABOUT THE ROOM, HE CLUTCHED WHAT HE THOUGHT WAS A HAND-RAIL—THEN...

CLICK

OOO-ER!

DIGBY HAD ACCIDENTALLY PULLED A WEAPON-FIRING LEVER. THE RESULT— CATASTROPHE!

EAGLE
AND Boys' World

8 May 1965   Vol. 16 No. 19   EVERY WEDNESDAY   6d.

DAN DARE
Pilot of the Future
in THE MOONSLEEPERS

Xel had set out with an armada of spaceships from Triton to invade Earth. Dan Dare and Digby had hidden themselves aboard one of his fleet, and their presence was a secret until Digby accidentally fired some missiles and hit the ship ahead!

XEL RAGED!

WHAT DIM-MINDED, SLEEP-SOAKED WRETCH DID THAT?

THE CULPRIT, ALBERT FITZWILLIAM DIGBY, WONDERED AT HIS OWN CLUMSINESS!

EEE! THAT'S PUT THE CAT AMONG THE PIGEONS!

THE DUTY TRITON SUDDENLY AWOKE...

M'MMM—AAA—AH!

BUT DAN DARE TOOK INSTANT ACTION!

AAAAH!

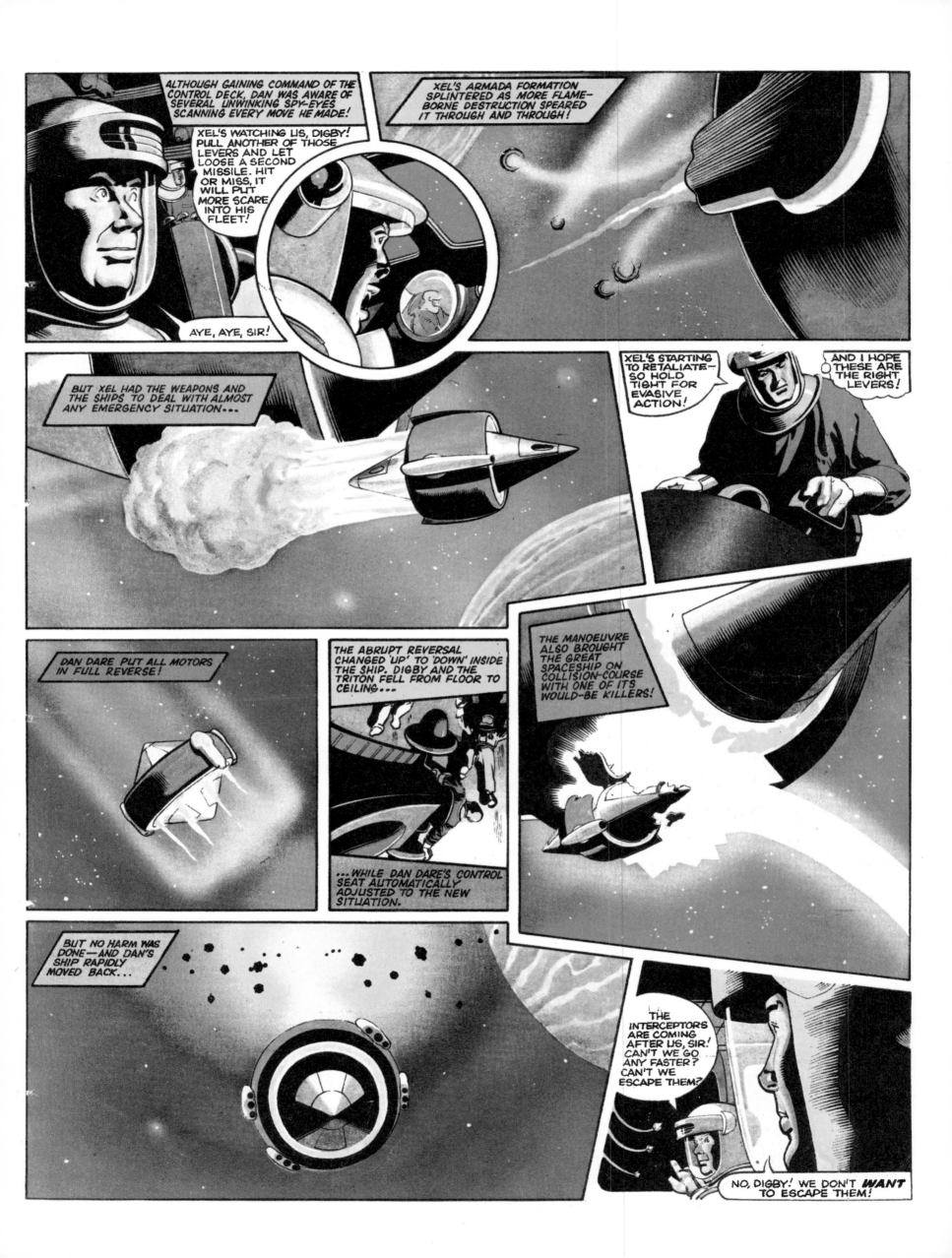

AS TRITON MISSILES SNAKED TOWARDS THEIR TARGET, DAN DARE BROKE THE STRANGLING GRIP . . .

NEAAAAH!

THE ASSAILANT COLLIDED WITH SEVERAL SWITCHES AND PITCHED THE GREAT SHIP INTO A CARTWHEEL SPIN — A MILLI-SECOND BEFORE THE MISSILES WOULD HAVE STRUCK!

THE TRITON ATTACK COMMANDER ORDERED WITHDRAWAL . . .

RETURN TO FLEET — WE ARE NOW AT THE EXTREME LIMIT OF OUR FUEL RANGE!

BUT THE CRAZY TUMBLING OF THE LARGE SPACESHIP CAUSED CHAOS IN THE CONTROL ROOM . . .

OOOH! NOW I KNOW HOW A DICE FEELS IN A GAME OF LUDO!

AND THERE WAS HAVOC IN THE CREW QUARTERS . . .

DESPITE THE SICKENING ACTIONS OF THE SHIP, SEVERAL TRITONS CLAWED THEIR WAY TO THE CENTRAL SHAFT . . . .

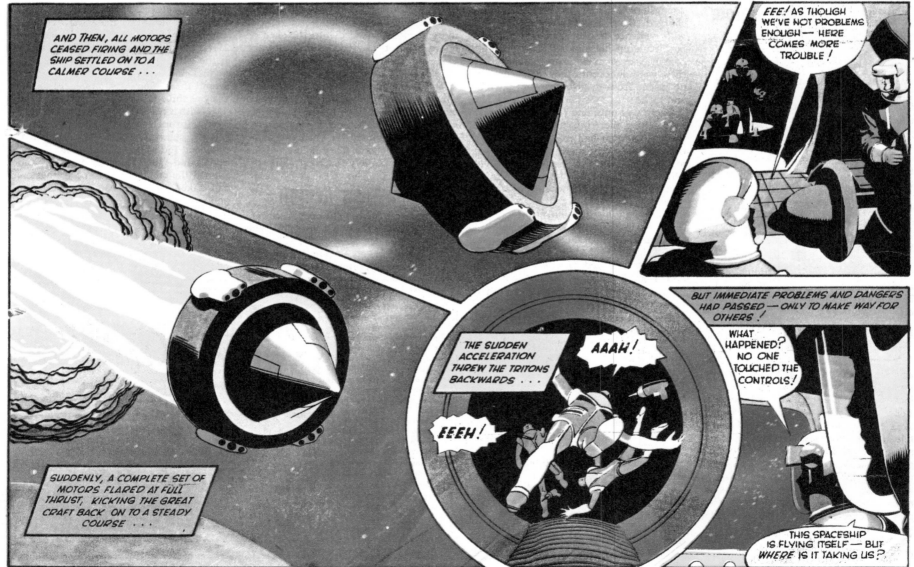

AND THEN, ALL MOTORS CEASED FIRING AND THE SHIP SETTLED ON TO A CALMER COURSE . . .

EEE! AS THOUGH WE'VE NOT PROBLEMS ENOUGH — HERE COMES MORE TROUBLE!

SUDDENLY, A COMPLETE SET OF MOTORS FLARED AT FULL THRUST, KICKING THE GREAT CRAFT BACK ON TO A STEADY COURSE . . .

THE SUDDEN ACCELERATION THREW THE TRITONS BACKWARDS . . .

AAAH!

EEEH!

BUT IMMEDIATE PROBLEMS AND DANGERS HAD PASSED — ONLY TO MAKE WAY FOR OTHERS!

WHAT HAPPENED? NO ONE TOUCHED THE CONTROLS!

THIS SPACESHIP IS FLYING ITSELF — BUT WHERE IS IT TAKING US?

EAGLE
AND Boys' World

22 May 1965 Vol. 16 No. 21   EVERY WEDNESDAY   6d.

DAN DARE
Pilot of the Future
in THE MOONSLEEPERS

Xel had amassed a fleet of spaceships and an army of Tritons, and was on his way to invade Earth. The Mekon had promised to attack Venus at the same moment. Dan Dare and Digby, stowaways in Xel's fleet, had managed to take over one of the ships and cause some havoc, but the ship suddenly began to steer itself . . .

INSIDE THE CONTROL ROOM OF THE TRITON SPACESHIP, DAN DARE AND DIGBY WERE BAFFLED...

EVERYTHING'S ON FULL AUTOMATIC! ALL THE MANUAL CONTROLS ARE DEAD!

AND THIS ASTROGATION SYSTEM IS TOO ALIEN FOR ME TO UNDERSTAND WHAT COURSE WE'RE TAKING!

IT'S A PITY ABOUT HIM! HE'D BE THE ONLY ONE TO TELL US HOW TO FLY THIS SHIP!

NOT THE ONLY ONE, DIGBY! THERE IS A HOLD FULL OF TRITON CREWMEN ON THE DECK BELOW US!

BUT THEY'RE ALL HOSTILE— AND WE'RE NOT ARMED!

JUST STAY WITH ME AND KEEP QUIET!

DAN JUMPED...

EEEEH!

EEEH!

DAN WOULD HAVE CRASHED WITH HIS ENEMIES TO THE DEPTHS OF THE SPACESHIP, BUT FOR THE QUICKNESS OF HIS HAND!

BUT...

DIGBY WAS NEAR...

THANKS, DIGBY! YOU COULD HAVE BEEN KILLED SAVING MY LIFE!

AYE—BUT SINCE YOU'RE THE ONLY ONE OF US WITH ANY IDEA HOW TO BREAK UP XEL'S INVASION PLANS, YOUR LIFE IS MORE VALUABLE THAN MINE!

THEN EVERYTHING HAPPENED FAST. TRITONS WERE SUDDENLY EVERYWHERE. DAN SCOOPED UP A GUN AND BLASTED INTO THE MOVING SHADOWS...

AND THE ALIEN ATTACKERS SCRAMBLED IN PANIC FOR SAFETY...

CAN YOU SEE HOW THEIR FOOD IS SUPPLIED?

AYE! IT COMES FROM A LOWER DECK INTO THOSE FEEDING MACHINES—BUT I CAN ALSO SEE TRITONS MOVING AROUND BEHIND US!

THEN WE WANT TO GO ONE DECK LOWER—WE'RE ON THE WRONG DECK HERE!

BY GUM— YOU'RE TELLING ME!

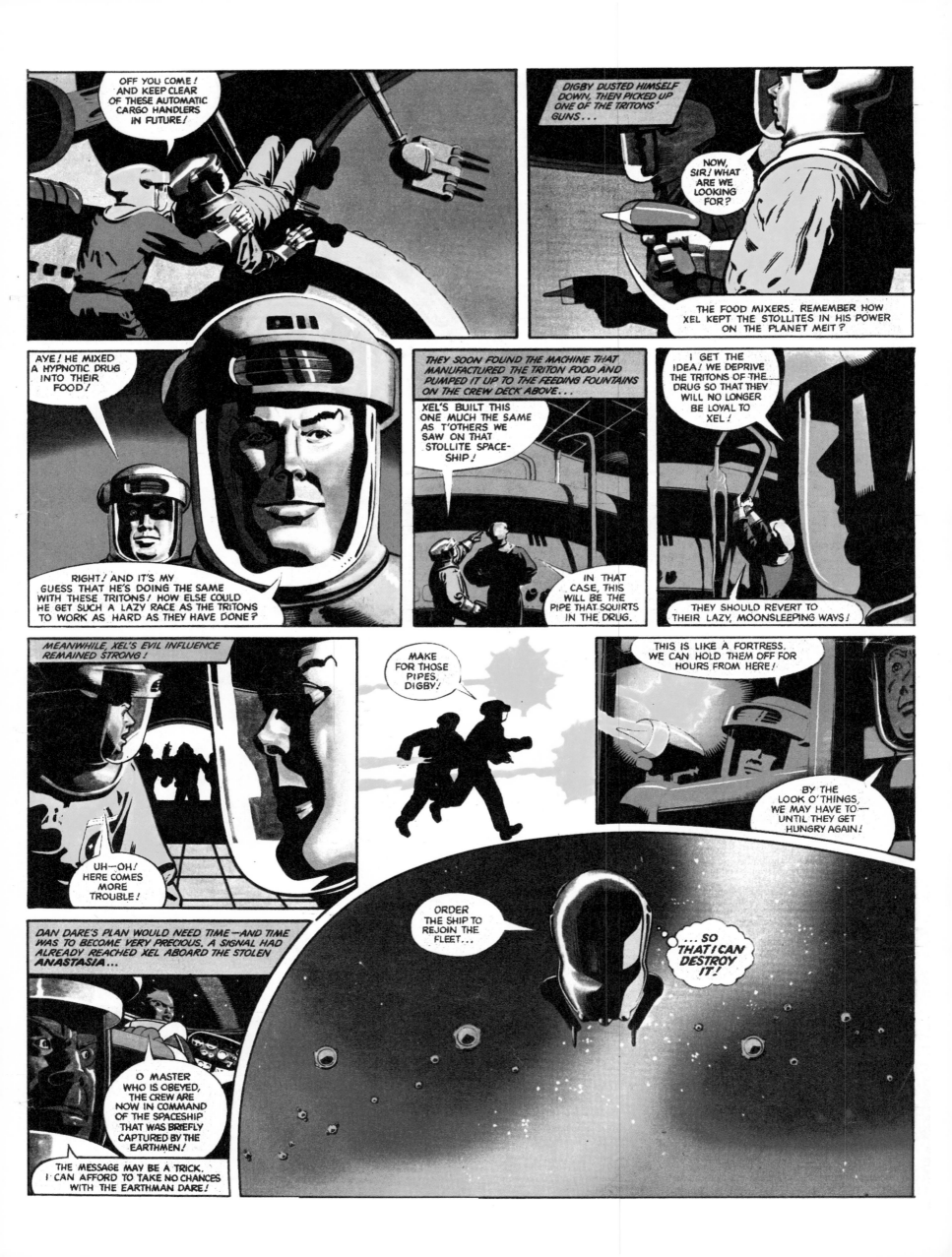

EAGLE
AND Boys' World

5 June 1965 Vol. 16 No. 23

EVERY WEDNESDAY 6d.

DAN DARE
Pilot of the Future
in THE MOONSLEEPERS

The crew of a Triton spaceship, bound for Earth with hostile intent, had cornered Dan Dare and Digby. The Tritons were normally sleepy and lazy, but were under a drug given to them by the evil Xel. This made them fierce and they attacked Dan and Digby with flame-throwers . . .

EEEE! THAT WERE A CLOSE ONE!

KEITH WATSON

IS THERE MUCH DAMAGE DONE, DIGBY?

NAY—NOWT BUT SEEPAGE!

AT THAT MOMENT, IN THE CONTROL ROOM...

THE COMMAND OF XEL, HE WHO IS OBEYED, IS THAT YOU REJOIN THE MAIN FLEET AT ONCE!

NO ONE SUSPECTED THAT THE REASON FOR THIS ORDER WAS TO ENABLE XEL TO DESTROY DAN DARE BY DESTROYING THE WHOLE SPACESHIP!

THE COURSE ALTERATION WAS MADE BY FIRING EXTRA MOTORS ON ONE SIDE OF THE SPACESHIP...

THIS MEANT THAT FUEL PRESSURE BUILT UP IN PIPES FEEDING THESE MOTORS—AND ONE SUDDENLY BURST...

AAAH!

THEN, FOR NO OBVIOUS REASON, THE VOLATILE FLUID FLARED!

INSTANTLY, FROM SOME FAR SECTION OF THE HOLD...

WHEEEE...

THE STRANGE MACHINE WAS A FIRE-FIGHTER...

THE TRITONS WHO HAD BEEN BESIEGING DAN AND DIGBY SUDDENLY SEEMED TO LOSE ALL INTEREST IN CONTINUING THE ATTACK...

FEELING HUNGRY, THEY TRICKLED AWAY TO FIND FOOD...

...WARMTH FOR THEIR BODIES, AND REST FOR THEIR LIMBS...

BY GUM—I'M GLAD THAT'S OVER! WHAT NEXT, SIR?

WE NOW FIND AN UNDRUGGED TRITON AND LEARN HOW TO CONTROL THIS SPACESHIP!

WHAT...?

SUDDENLY...

OOO—EEEE!

DAN HAD CUT OFF THE SUPPLY OF DRUGS BY WHICH XEL KEPT THE TRITONS UNDER HIS POWER, AND WITHOUT IT, THE MOONSLEEPERS REVERTED TO THEIR NORMAL, EASY-GOING WAYS...

YOUR PLAN HAS WORKED SO FAR, SIR! THEY'RE NOT ATTACKING US ANY MORE!

THEY ARE SCARED OF US— JUST AS THEY WERE ON TRITON!

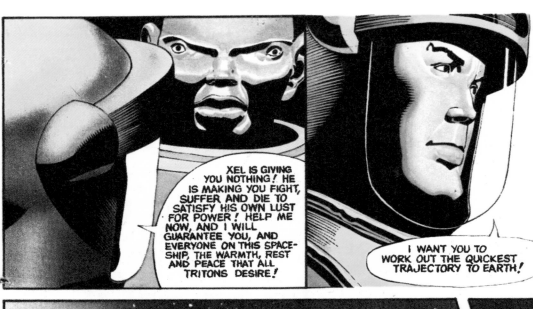

XEL IS GIVING YOU NOTHING! HE IS MAKING YOU FIGHT, SUFFER AND DIE TO SATISFY HIS OWN LUST FOR POWER! HELP ME NOW, AND I WILL GUARANTEE YOU, AND EVERYONE ON THIS SPACE-SHIP, THE WARMTH, REST AND PEACE THAT ALL TRITONS DESIRE!

I WANT YOU TO WORK OUT THE QUICKEST TRAJECTORY TO EARTH!

THE TRITONS OBEYED. IT WAS EASIER THAN ARGUING...

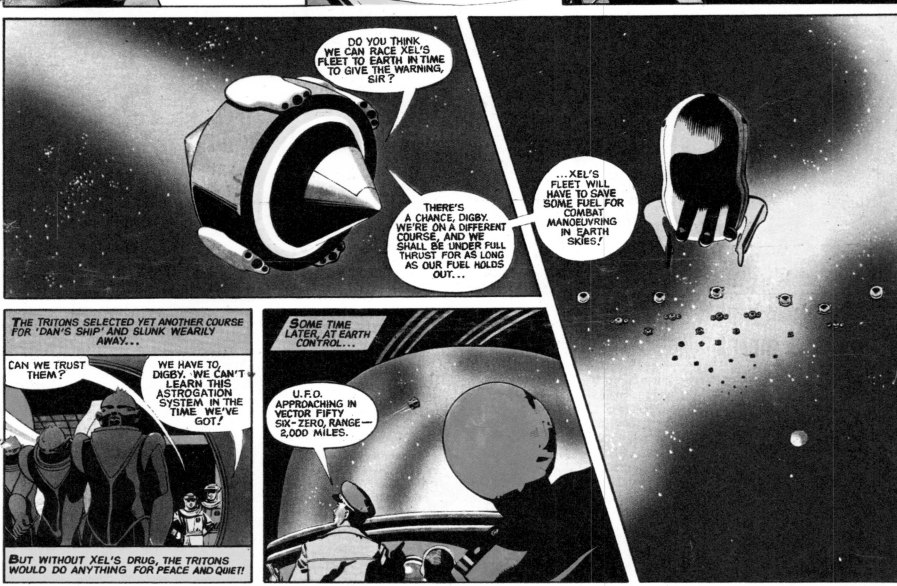

DO YOU THINK WE CAN RACE XEL'S FLEET TO EARTH IN TIME TO GIVE THE WARNING, SIR?

THERE'S A CHANCE, DIGBY. WE'RE ON A DIFFERENT COURSE, AND WE SHALL BE UNDER FULL THRUST FOR AS LONG AS OUR FUEL HOLDS OUT...

...XEL'S FLEET WILL HAVE TO SAVE SOME FUEL FOR COMBAT MANOEUVRING IN EARTH SKIES!

THE TRITONS SELECTED YET ANOTHER COURSE FOR 'DAN'S SHIP' AND SLUNK WEARILY AWAY...

CAN WE TRUST THEM?

WE HAVE TO, DIGBY. WE CAN'T LEARN THIS ASTROGATION SYSTEM IN THE TIME WE'VE GOT!

BUT WITHOUT XEL'S DRUG, THE TRITONS WOULD DO ANYTHING FOR PEACE AND QUIET!

SOME TIME LATER, AT EARTH CONTROL...

U.F.O. APPROACHING IN VECTOR FIFTY SIX-ZERO, RANGE — 2,000 MILES.

HAVE TRIED ALL REGULAR SYSTEMS FOR IDENTIFICATION — BUT CAN GET NO RESPONSE...

IT COULD BE HOSTILE. ALERT PROCEDURE — PROGRAMME ONE!

INTERCEPTOR SQUADRON ALPHA, ALPHA — SCRAMBLE!

EAGLE
AND Boys' World

19 June 1965 Vol. 16 No. 25

EVERY WEDNESDAY 6d.

DAN DARE
Pilot of the Future

in THE MOONSLEEPERS

Dan Dare and Digby had taken control of a Triton spaceship – one of a fleet sent by Xel to invade the Earth. Dan had raced the fleet to Earth, but as he entered home skies, the defence squadrons intercepted, believing Dan's ship to be hostile, and he had no means of telling them otherwise . . .

KEITH WATSON

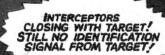

INTERCEPTORS CLOSING WITH TARGET! STILL NO IDENTIFICATION SIGNAL FROM TARGET!

MISSILES LOCKED-ON AND READY FOR 'GO'. PROGRAMME ONE COMPLETE!

STAND BY FOR PROGRAMME TWO!

PROGRAMME ONE WAS MERELY 'ALERT PROCEDURE'. PROGRAMME TWO WAS 'INTERCEPT AND DESTROY'...

THE INTERCEPTORS ARE HOMING ON US, SIR! THEY'LL SOON BE SHOOTING!

THEN THE LONGER WE REMAIN IN SPACE, THE MORE DANGEROUS IT WILL BE!

OUR BEST MOVE WILL BE TO LAND AS QUICKLY AS POSSIBLE AND GIVE THOSE INTERCEPTORS LITTLE CHANCE TO GET AT US!

AYE, SIR, BUT THOSE INTERCEPTOR SQUADRONS ARE GOOD— THEY'VE NEVER MISSED A TARGET YET!

CONTROL TO ALPHA, ALPHA LEADER— FIRE!

THAT'S OUR LAST CHANCE—THE WARNING SHOT TO MAKE US TURN AWAY!

BUT DAN KNEW THAT EVEN IF HE TURNED THE SHIP AWAY, DESTRUCTION WOULD STILL FOLLOW UNLESS HE COULD IDENTIFY HIMSELF...

WE'VE GOT TO KEEP GOING, DIGBY—AND GET ONE OF THE CREW UP HERE. WE'LL NEED HELP TO LAND THIS THING!

UNLESS WE'RE ALL BLOWN TO BITS FIRST!

MORE MISSILES COMING—HOLD TIGHT FOR EVASIVE ACTION!

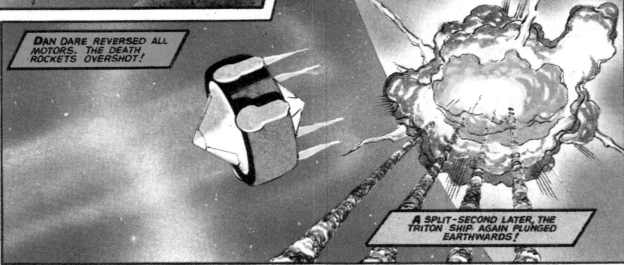

DAN DARE REVERSED ALL MOTORS. THE DEATH ROCKETS OVERSHOT!

A SPLIT-SECOND LATER, THE TRITON SHIP AGAIN PLUNGED EARTHWARDS!

DAN HAD SAVED THE SHIP, EVEN THOUGH THE ABRUPT MANOEUVRE HAD BATTERED MORE THAN HALF THE UNPREPARED TRITON CREW INTO UNCONSCIOUSNESS...

COME ON, CHUM! YOU'RE FIT FOR DUTY—UPSTAIRS!

IT'S TOO NEAR! A DIRECT HIT NOW WOULD SHOWER THE EARTH WITH RADIO-ACTIVE DEBRIS.

CONTROL TO ALPHA, ALPHA LEADER—STOP FIRING! TARGET WITHIN FALL-OUT RANGE!

WE'RE HEADING FOR EAST ANGLIA!

TRY FOR A LANDING IN THE FENS—THIS GREEN AREA!

I WILL TRY!

BUT XEL'S BRIEF TRAINING HAD NOT MADE THE TRITON PILOT AN EXPERT!

WE'RE GOING FOR THE SEA—I CANNOT CONTROL OUR DIRECTION!

GET OUT OF THE WAY—I'LL TAKE OVER!

A FEW MILES SOUTH OF CROMER...

LOOK, DAD! A SPACE-SHIP!

EH? IT'S COMING THIS WAY—RIGHT AT US!

EAGLE
AND Boys' World

26 June 1965   VOL. 16 No. 26   EVERY WEDNESDAY   6d.

DAN DARE
Pilot of the Future
in THE MOONSLEEPERS

Dan Dare and Digby were racing towards Earth in a Triton spaceship to give warning of an approaching alien invasion armada led by Xel. Dan Dare was barely able to control the strange spaceship as it skimmed towards a crowded holiday beach, but disaster was narrowly averted...

THE LOWER POINT OF THE SPACESHIP HINGED OPEN. STEPS FELL INTO THE WAVES AND TWO MEN EMERGED...

WE'RE BACK IN TIME FOR THE HOLIDAY SEASON!

I'D HAVE BROUGHT MY WATER-WINGS HAD I KNOWN!

WITHIN SECONDS, SPACE FLEET JET-COPTERS WERE CONVERGING ON THE INTRUDER FROM SPACE...

MOST OF THE ALIEN CREW HAD BEEN SHAKEN AND INJURED BY THE WILD LANDING...

I MADE A PROMISE THAT THEY WOULD BE LOOKED AFTER— SO FEED THEM, REST THEM, AND KEEP THEM WARM!

VERY GOOD, COLONEL DARE!

NOW GET ME TO SPACE-FLEET H.Q.—THERE'S THE WHOLE WORLD TO BE SAVED YET!

LATER, AT THE HEADQUARTERS CONFERENCE ROOM...

OUR ENEMIES PLAN TO ATTACK EARTH AND VENUS AT THE SAME MOMENT, THEREBY PREVENTING ONE PLANET COMING TO THE ASSISTANCE OF THE OTHER!

WE ARE CERTAIN THAT XEL'S FLEET OUTNUMBERS EARTH DEFENCE FORCES, AND, JUST AS PROBABLY, THE MEKON'S STRENGTH IS SUPERIOR TO THAT ON VENUS...

WHERE HAS THE MEKON OBTAINED SUCH FORCES, SIR?

A GOOD QUESTION, MAJOR SPENCE.

I BELIEVE THAT HE WILL NOT ATTACK VENUS UNTIL LONG AFTER XEL HAS ATTACKED EARTH, AND WHEN THE THERON DEFENCE FORCES HAVE BEEN WITHDRAWN FROM VENUS TO HELP US!

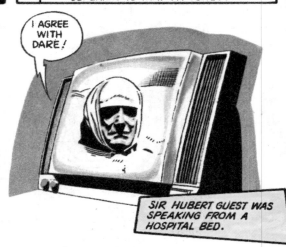

I AGREE WITH DARE!

SIR HUBERT GUEST WAS SPEAKING FROM A HOSPITAL BED.

I SUGGEST WE CALL THE THERON FLEET TO EARTH NOW! XEL WILL BE DEFEATED ALL THE QUICKER, AND THE THERON AND EARTH SHIPS CAN RUSH TO VENUS AFTERWARDS FOR THE BATTLE AGAINST THE MEKON!

THE PLAN WAS A GAMBLE STAKED ON THE MEKON'S TREACHERY, BUT THE COMMITTEE APPROVED IT AS THE ONLY SCHEME THAT OFFERED A PROMISE OF SUCCESS AGAINST SUPERIOR FORCES. SO, THE THERON FLEET LEFT VENUS...

EARTH PATROLS ROVED IN DEEP DEFENSIVE ORBITS, USING SENSITIVE SEARCH INSTRUMENTS TO PROBE FOR XEL'S ARMADA...

THE ALIEN FLEET WAS STEADILY APPROACHING...

... AND EARTH WAS GLOWING LIKE A TEMPTING GREEN FRUIT ON THE VIDEO SCREENS...

ALL CREWS PREPARE FOR BATTLE STATIONS!

EAGLE
AND Boys' World
3 July 1965 Vol. 16 No. 27

EVERY WEDNESDAY 6d.

DAN DARE
Pilot of the Future
in THE MOONSLEEPERS

Xel was approaching Earth with an invasion armada of Tritons. It was feared that the Mekon also planned to attack Venus, but the Theron defences of Venus were speeding to Earth in the belief that Xel would make the first attack. The heavens were being scoured for the attackers . . .

THE FIRST REPORT CAME FROM THE SPACE-FLEET BASE ON THE MOON . . .

ALIEN SHIPS LOCATED— DESTINATION EARTH!

KEITH WATSON

THE NEAREST PATROL SHIPS MANOEUVRED TO INTERCEPT . . .

FOR STAND-BY CREWS ON EARTH, THE 'ALERT', 'SCRAMBLE' AND 'LAUNCH' CALLS CAME WITHIN SECONDS OF EACH OTHER . . .

LEADING THE PROCESSION OF SPACESHIPS FROM THE PADS WAS ONE PILOTED BY COLONEL DAN DARE . . .!

SOME TIME LATER . . .

PATROL SHIP OMEGA 7. HAVE MADE CONTACT WITH HOSTILE ALIEN FLEET. POSITION IS . . . AAH!

SILENCE! SO OMEGA 7 IS XEL'S FIRST VICTIM!

EAGLE
AND Boys' World

10 July 1965   VOL. 16 No. 28   EVERY WEDNESDAY   6d.

DAN DARE
Pilot of the Future
in THE MOONSLEEPERS

Dan Dare was fighting a desperate space battle to prevent Xel and his Triton invasion fleet from breaking through to Earth. Xel ordered his numerically superior fleet to scatter, knowing that *some* spaceships would reach their objective untouched . . .

KEITH WATSON

COLONEL DARE TO ALL COMMANDERS! HUNT IN PAIRS! PURSUE AND DESTROY AS MANY OF THE ENEMY AS POSSIBLE! REMEMBER, THE FOLKS AT HOME ARE DEPENDING ON US!

BUT THE TRITON DEFENCE SCREEN OF SMALLER, FASTER SPACESHIPS CLOSED IN ON THE EARTH INTERCEPTORS . . .

FIRE ONE! FIRE TWO!

A HIT!

AND YET ANOTHER OF DAN'S VITAL FLEET DISINTEGRATED . . .

FRIENDLY THERON REINFORCEMENTS FROM VENUS WERE STREAKING TO DAN'S AID—BUT, AS YET, SPACE SEEMED FILLED WITH ENEMIES!

THREE TRITONS COMING IN AT TWO O'CLOCK, SIR!

HOLD ON FOR SOME TIGHT MANOEUVRING!

DAN FIRED HIS RETRO-ROCKETS AT FULL THRUST...

THIS ACTION THREW MORE THAN THE ENEMY INTO VIOLENT CONFUSION....!

WE'VE PULLED OUT OF THE LINE OF ATTACK!

YEEE-OW! WHAT THE HECK!

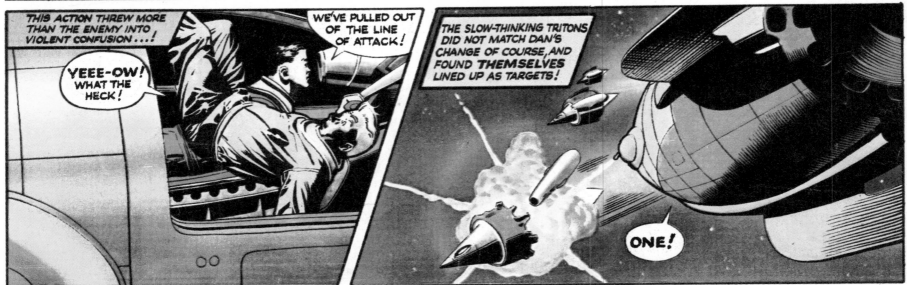

THE SLOW-THINKING TRITONS DID NOT MATCH DAN'S CHANGE OF COURSE, AND FOUND THEMSELVES LINED UP AS TARGETS!

ONE!

TWO!

WE'RE GOING TO COLLIDE WITH NUMBER THREE!

UNABLE TO SWERVE IN TIME TO AVOID THE TRITON SHIP, DAN FIRED POINT-BLANK INTO IT, AND CRASHED THROUGH THE FLYING DEBRIS...

WE'RE ON FIRE, SIR!

WORSE THAN THAT, DIGBY! LOOK AT THAT SMOKE RUSHING OUT—WE'RE HOLED! WE'RE LOSING OUR AIR!

EAGLE AND Boys' World

17 July 1965 Vol. 16 No. 29

EVERY WEDNESDAY 6d.

DAN DARE
Pilot of the Future
in THE MOONSLEEPERS

Engaged in a desperate battle with Xel's Triton invasion fleet, Dan Dare's spaceship cockpit was set on fire and the air-tight canopy holed . . .

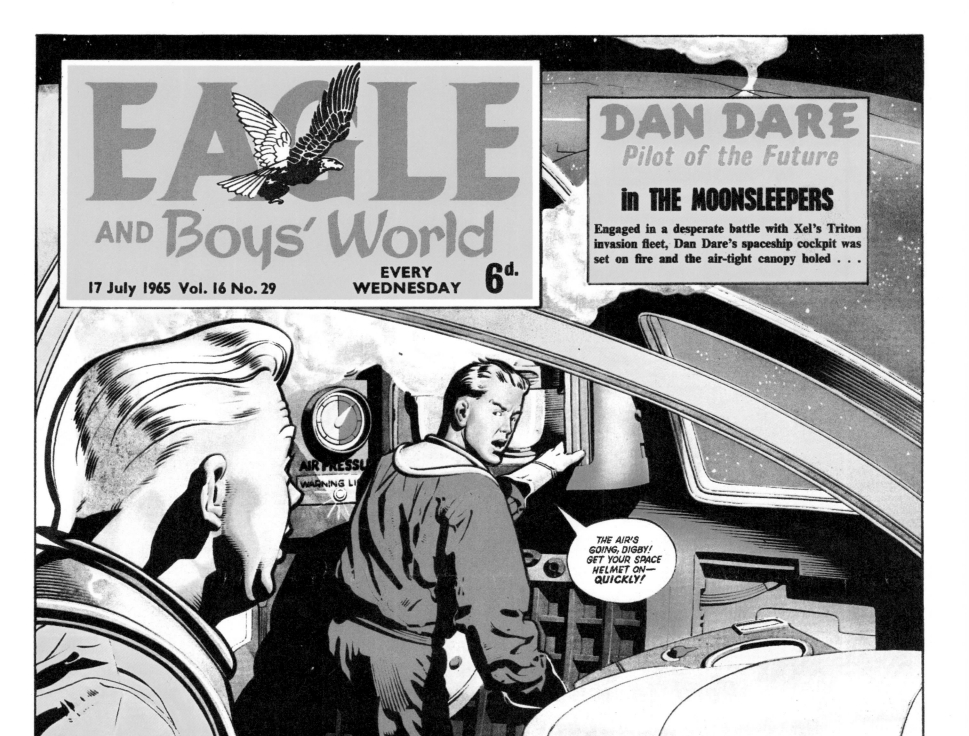

THE AIR'S GOING, DIGBY! GET YOUR SPACE HELMET ON— QUICKLY!

THE MEN HAD SECONDS ONLY FOR SURVIVAL....!

THERE'S NO AIR—I CAN'T BREATHE—I HAVEN'T GOT THE STRENGTH TO—TO...

DAN PRESSED HOME HIS HELMET, AND A SECOND LATER, THE SUIT'S CANNED OXYGEN RELIEVED HIS TORTURED LUNGS. HAZILY, HE SAW DIGBY STAGGER, HIS HELMET BOBBING LOOSE. HE LUNGED FOR HIM...

GU-UUUUH!

IT MUST SEAL FIRST TIME—IT MUST!

THANKS, SIR— BUT, BY GUM, THAT WERE A NASTY MOMENT, WHAT WI' FIRE AND LOSING OUR AIR...

THAT'S ONE GOOD THING ABOUT A VACUUM— FIRE CAN'T BURN IN IT...

BUT WE'VE NO HOPE OF CATCHING THOSE TRITONS. THEY'LL REACH EARTH, AND WE CAN'T STOP THEM!

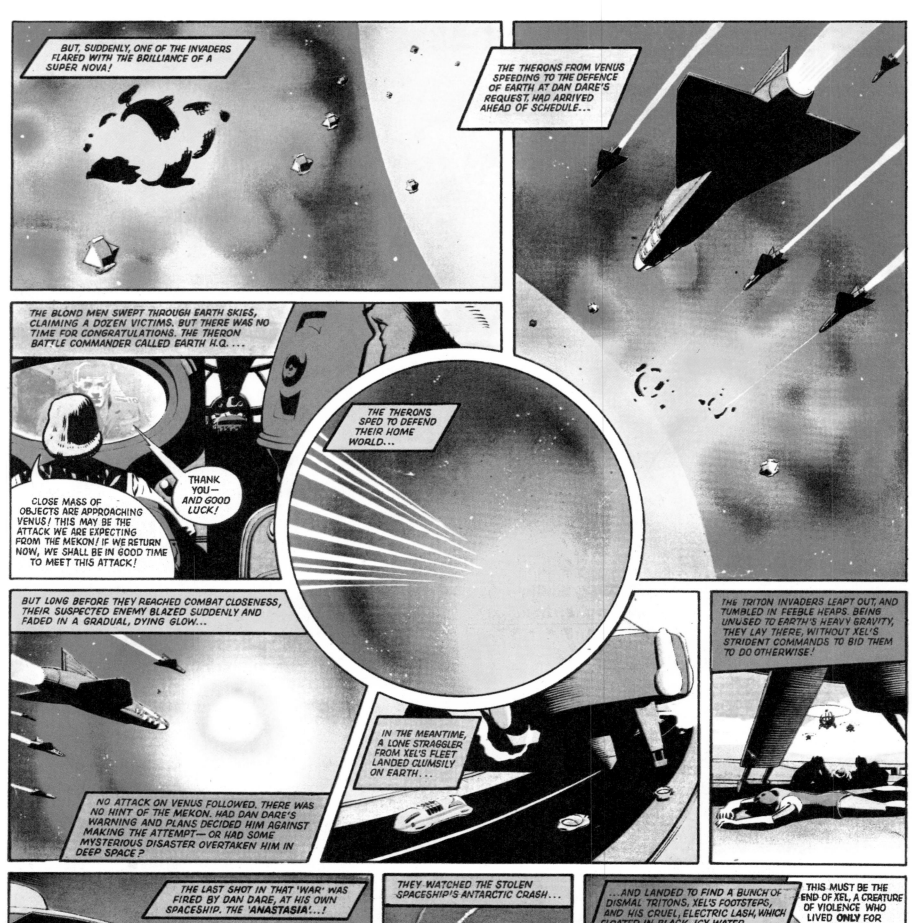

BUT, SUDDENLY, ONE OF THE INVADERS FLARED WITH THE BRILLIANCE OF A SUPER NOVA!

THE THERONS FROM VENUS SPEEDING TO THE DEFENCE OF EARTH AT DAN DARE'S REQUEST, HAD ARRIVED AHEAD OF SCHEDULE...

THE BLOND MEN SWEPT THROUGH EARTH SKIES, CLAIMING A DOZEN VICTIMS. BUT THERE WAS NO TIME FOR CONGRATULATIONS. THE THERON BATTLE COMMANDER CALLED EARTH H.Q....

CLOSE MASS OF OBJECTS ARE APPROACHING VENUS! THIS MAY BE THE ATTACK WE ARE EXPECTING FROM THE MEKON! IF WE RETURN NOW, WE SHALL BE IN GOOD TIME TO MEET THIS ATTACK!

THANK YOU— AND GOOD LUCK!

THE THERONS SPED TO DEFEND THEIR HOME WORLD...

BUT LONG BEFORE THEY REACHED COMBAT CLOSENESS, THEIR SUSPECTED ENEMY BLAZED SUDDENLY AND FADED IN A GRADUAL, DYING GLOW...

NO ATTACK ON VENUS FOLLOWED. THERE WAS NO HINT OF THE MEKON. HAD DAN DARE'S WARNING AND PLANS DECIDED HIM AGAINST MAKING THE ATTEMPT— OR HAD SOME MYSTERIOUS DISASTER OVERTAKEN HIM IN DEEP SPACE?

IN THE MEANTIME, A LONE STRAGGLER FROM XEL'S FLEET LANDED CLUMSILY ON EARTH...

THE TRITON INVADERS LEAPT OUT, AND TUMBLED IN FEEBLE HEAPS. BEING UNUSED TO EARTH'S HEAVY GRAVITY, THEY LAY THERE, WITHOUT XEL'S STRIDENT COMMANDS TO BID THEM TO DO OTHERWISE!

THE LAST SHOT IN THAT 'WAR' WAS FIRED BY DAN DARE, AT HIS OWN SPACESHIP. THE 'ANASTASIA'...!

THEY WATCHED THE STOLEN SPACESHIP'S ANTARCTIC CRASH...

...AND LANDED TO FIND A BUNCH OF DISMAL TRITONS, XEL'S FOOTSTEPS, AND HIS CRUEL, ELECTRIC LASH, WHICH FLOATED IN BLACK, ICY WATER...

THIS MUST BE THE END OF XEL, A CREATURE OF VIOLENCE WHO LIVED ONLY FOR VIOLENCE!

AYE, AND GOOD RIDDANCE, I SAY! NOW LET'S GET TO SOME PLACE WHERE IT'S SUMMER!

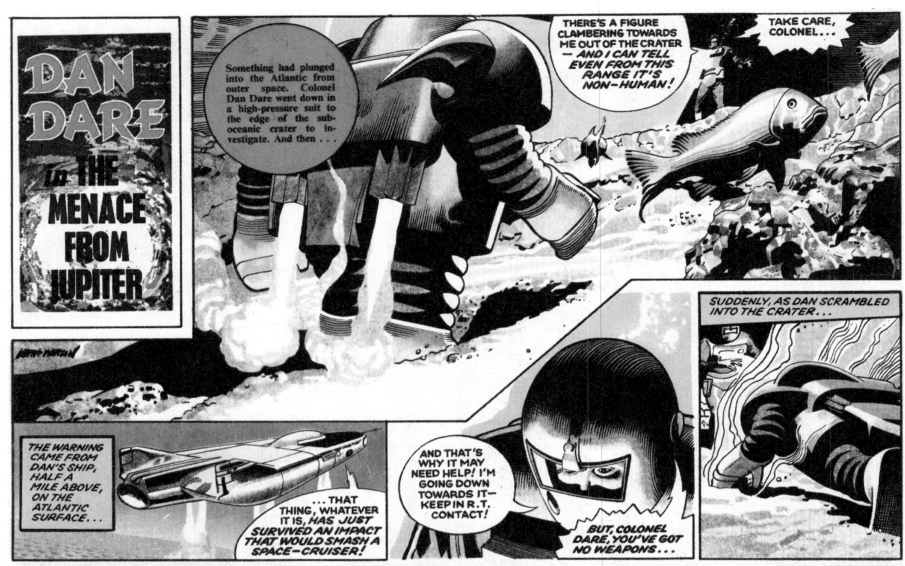

DAN DARE
in THE MENACE FROM JUPITER

Colonel Dan Dare, investigating a ship which had plunged into the Atlantic from outer space, had found, on the sea-bed, a strange alien so massive that the motor powering the lifting-grab on Dan's rescue ship had seized. So emergency tactics were employed . . .

DON'T WORRY, FRIEND — WE'RE GETTING YOU CLEAR OF THIS BY USING SHEER ROCKET-POWER TO LIFT EVERYTHING UP!

LET US HOPE YOUR PUNY CABLE CAN STAND THE STRAIN OF MY MASSIVE WEIGHT . . .

SLOWLY, STEADILY, THE SPACESHIP BLASTED UP, UNTIL AT LAST, DANGLING IN CLEAR AIR ON THE END OF THE HALF-MILE CABLE . . . .

I'VE SENT AN URGENT MAYDAY CALL FOR HELP, COLONEL DARE!

THE SOONER THE BETTER — WE'RE SWINGING ON THIS DARNED THING LIKE A PENDULUM!

IF THIS CABLE SNAPS NOW, I WILL PLUNGE DEEP INTO THE CRUST OF YOUR PLANET . . .

WE'RE PRAYING THAT IT WON'T!

AT LAST, THE RESCUE FLEET ARRIVED . . .

DARE GETS HIMSELF INTO SOME STRANGE SITUATIONS!

O.K., SCOUT SHIP — YOU CAN RELAX. WE'RE TAKING OVER!

THE ALIEN WAS SWUNG INTO A SPECIAL ARMOURED BAY . . .

IS IT SAFE TO WALK ON THIS — FRAGILE SUBSTANCE?

THANKS, DIGBY — THAT WAS A NEAR THING!

THE LOAD ON THE CABLE, SIR, WAS ONE HUNDRED TONS! IT'S FANTASTIC!

WHEN THE REPULSORS ON MY SUIT ARE REPAIRED, MY WEIGHT WILL THEN SEEM NORMAL AGAIN BY YOUR STANDARDS — BUT UNTIL THEN, LET US GO WITH CARE!

YOU ARE FROM A PLANET WITH A HIGH GRAVITATIONAL FIELD?

YES — I AM FROM JUPITER!

I HAVE COME HERE FOR HELP. A RACE OF GIANT CREATURES IS INVADING THE SOLAR SYSTEM FROM OUTER SPACE! THEY HAVE ATTACKED JUPITER AND TURNED MY OWN RACE INTO SLAVES!

I, BRO, ALSO COME TO WARN YOU. WHEN THESE GIANTS HAVE CONQUERED JUPITER, THEY WILL THEN ATTACK EARTH!

DAN DARE
in THE MENACE FROM JUPITER

It was the Earth fleet's first contact, just past Mars, with a scoutship of the giant *Pittars* who had invaded Jupiter from outer space. And as the far-distant ship, only just detectable on the long-range screens, hurled out a shoal of missiles, Colonel Dan Dare loosed off a nuclear torpedo...

THE POINT IS, BRO — WILL OUR OWN WEAPON BE ABLE TO GET THROUGH?

THOUGH THEY HAVE ATTACKED YOU, DANDERR, THEY MAY NOT BE EXPECTING ATTACK. THEY BELIEVE IN CUNNING AND SURPRISE...

THE STUMPY LITTLE VERAN WAS GRIM BEHIND HIS VISOR...

...MY OWN PEOPLE WERE KINDLY AND PEACEFUL, AND THE PITTARS DESTROYED ALL OUR FLEETS WITHOUT WARNING — AS THEY NOW HOPE TO DESTROY YOU!

DON'T WORRY, BRO — WE'RE READY FOR THEM!

TEN MINUTES LATER. THE AUTOMATIC ALARM SOUNDED...

COLONEL DARE — THE ENEMY MISSILES HAVE JUST HURTLED THROUGH OUR LONG-RANGE DETECTOR SCREEN!

THEN GIVE THEM A DOSE OF THEIR OWN MEDICINE!

FROM THE EARTH FLEET BLASTED AN ARMADA OF ANTI-MISSILES...

A SUDDEN AND DEADLY FIREWORKS DISPLAY IN DEEP SPACE, WITNESSED BY DAN ON THE CONTROL ROOM VIEWER...

WELL, THAT PROVES THAT WHEREVER THE PITTARS COME FROM, WE'VE GOT AN ANSWER FOR THEIR WEAPONS!

V. ZAITSEV

COMPUTER MAINTEN

VISTA FORWARD

AND THEN A GREAT BALEFUL GLARE OF FIERCE ENERGY OUT OF THE FAR DISTANCE...

OUR OWN WEAPON, SIR — THE DETECTORS REGISTER A DIRECT HIT!

LET'S MOVE IN TO INSPECT THE DAMAGE!

AS THE EARTH FLEET STREAKED TOWARDS THE GLOW...

TEN MINUTES LATER, THE EFFECT OF THE NUCLEAR TORPEDO WAS BEING INSPECTED FROM CLOSE RANGE ON THE SCREENS..

YES, SIR, A KNOCKOUT HIT — AND LUCKY FOR US!

WE'LL GO OVER THERE WITH A BOARDING PARTY — IF ONLY TO GRASP THE SCALE OF WHAT WE'RE LOOKING AT!

PREPARE FOR A SHOCK, DANDERR — THESE PITTARS ARE TRULY GIANT! AS YOU GET NEARER TO THEIR SCOUTSHIP, YOU WILL LEARN WHAT THIS MEANS...

THE SHATTERED PITTAR SHIP WAS SO IMMENSE THAT DAN'S FLAGSHIP WAS FLOATING ALONGSIDE LIKE A MINNOW IN THE SHADOW OF A WHALE!

SO THIS IS THE SORT OF THING WE'LL BE UP AGAINST ON JUPITER!

DAN DARE and THE MENACE FROM JUPITER

Little Bro came from Jupiter to Earth to seek help against the giants invading his planet. On the way there, Dan Dare crippled one of the enemy ships and then approached it . . .

COME ON, DIGBY— LET'S BOARD, AND INSPECT!

SPACE SUIT LOCKERS

WILL THAT BE WISE, DANDERR?

THEY HAVE THOUSANDS OF SHIPS LIKE THIS, DANDERR! MY OWN PEOPLE, THE VERANS, WERE POWERLESS AGAINST THEM!

SO THIS IS THE SORT OF THING WE'LL BE UP AGAINST WHEN WE GET TO JUPITER?

NO G-FIELD—OUR MISSILE MUST HAVE SHATTERED THEIR POWER!

IF THERE WERE A G-FIELD, IT WOULD BE SO POWERFUL THAT AN EARTHMAN WOULD BE HELPLESS!

TAKING BRO, THE LITTLE VERAN, WITH THEM, DAN AND DIGBY FLOATED TOWARDS THE SHATTERED HULL...

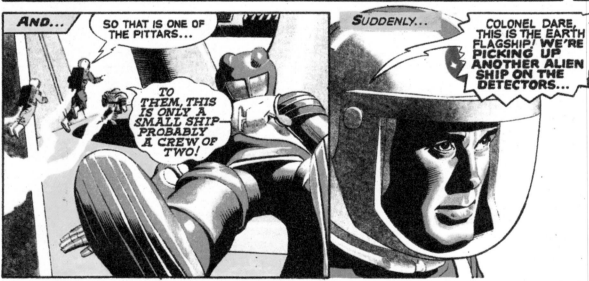

AND...

SO THAT IS ONE OF THE PITTARS...

TO THEM, THIS IS ONLY A SMALL SHIP— PROBABLY A CREW OF TWO!

SUDDENLY...

COLONEL DARE, THIS IS THE EARTH FLAGSHIP! WE'RE PICKING UP ANOTHER ALIEN SHIP ON THE DETECTORS...

BEFORE DAN COULD REPLY TO THE URGENT MESSAGE...

ON DAN'S FLAGSHIP, THERE WAS CONSTERNATION...

COLONEL DARE—WE'RE UNDER ATTACK! THE ARGUS HAS BEEN HIT BY A MISSILE, BUT NOT SERIOUSLY...

O.K.—I'M RECEIVING YOU! WE'VE NO TIME TO GET OFF THIS HULK, SO WE'LL STAY WHERE WE ARE! TAKE THE FLEET OUT OF DANGER, AND TRACK THE ALIEN ON THE SCREENS!

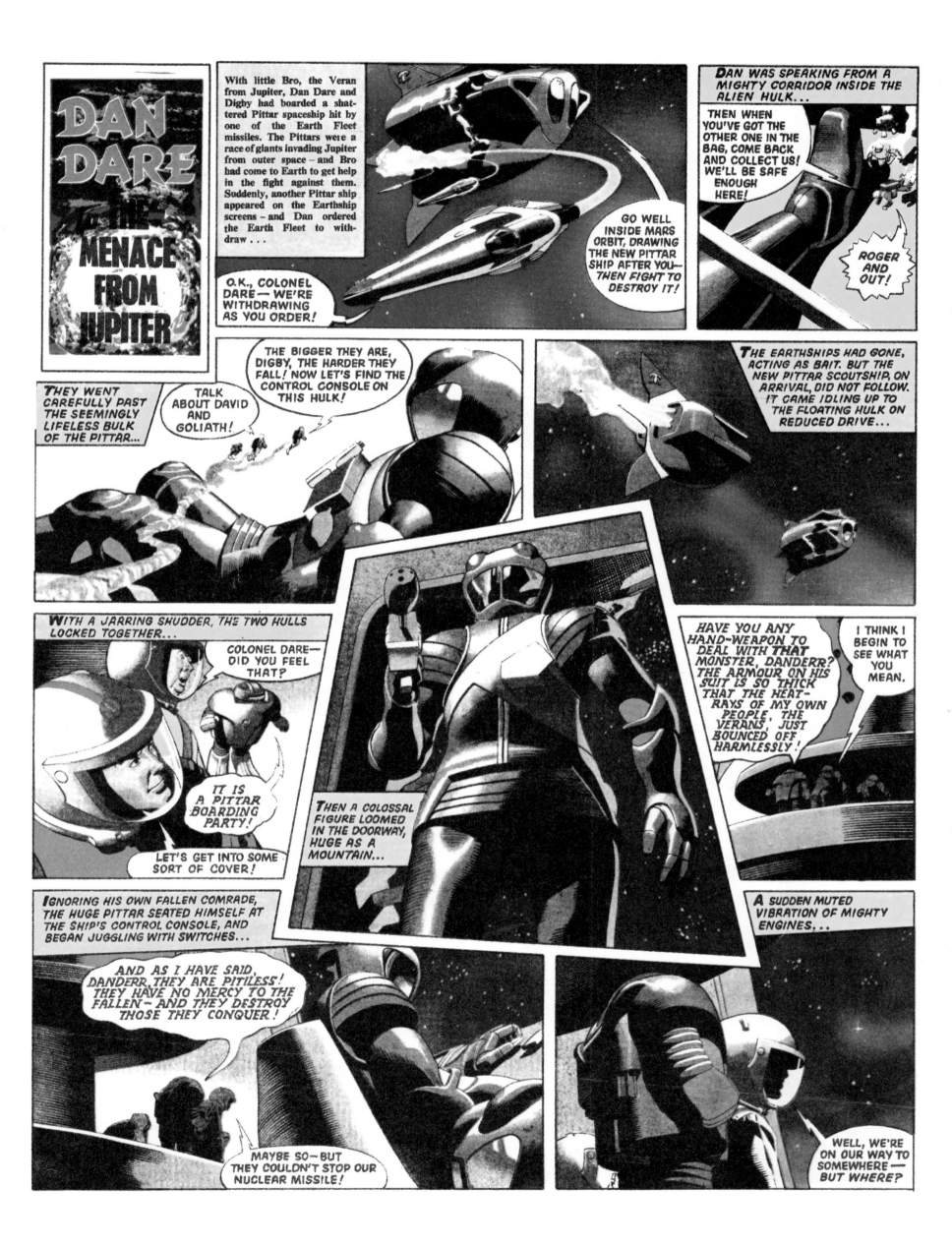

DAN DARE in THE MENACE FROM JUPITER

On board the crippled Pittar ship, a reeling giant groped wildly as a multitude of tiny blaster-shots from Colonel Dan Dare and Digby starred the visor on his helmet . . .

WE'RE IN A VACUUM BECAUSE OF THE HOLE OUR MISSILE BLASTED IN THIS SHIP'S SIDE—SO HE CAN'T TAKE OFF HIS HELMET!

AND IF HE CAN'T SEE, WE'VE GOT HIM AT OUR MERCY!

A SUDDEN RT SHOUT FROM BRO, THE LITTLE VERAN . . .

THE PITTAR IS SIGNALLING HIS OTHER SCOUTSHIP— I CAN PICK HIM UP ON MY SPECIAL WAVELENGTHS... HE IS TELLING THE OTHER PITTAR— THERE IS ONLY ONE OTHER— ABOUT US!

THE BLINDED PITTAR GROPED HIS WAY ACROSS THE CONTROL ROOM...

HE IS BEING TOLD TO ABANDON THIS SHIP! THEY WILL THEN MOVE OFF TO A DISTANCE, AND DESTROY IT WITH MISSILES!

WEIGHTLESS, DAN LAUNCHED HIMSELF UP...

NOT IF I CAN HELP IT! COME ON, BRO—LET'S GET TO THE CONTROL PANEL!

AN INSTANT LATER...

WE'VE GOT SECONDS IN WHICH TO ACT— I WANT INSTANT ACCELERATION!

YES, I KNOW THE PITTAR CONTROL SYSTEMS WELL! IF WE CAN MOVE THAT LEVER AS FAR AS IT WILL GO...

AND WITH THE EXERTION OF TREMENDOUS FORCE...

O.K.— IT'S YIELDING...

MOVE- IT-AS- FAR-AS- POSSIBLE!

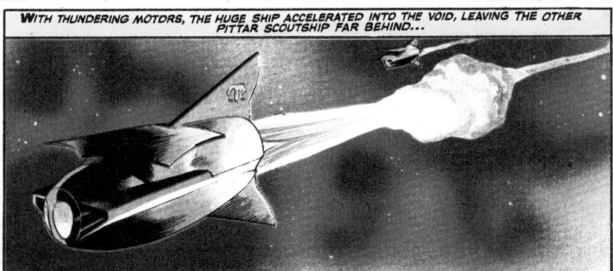

WITH THUNDERING MOTORS, THE HUGE SHIP ACCELERATED INTO THE VOID, LEAVING THE OTHER PITTAR SCOUTSHIP FAR BEHIND...

AND IT WAS AT THAT INSTANT THAT THE BLINDED PITTAR HAD LAUNCHED HIMSELF AT WHERE THE OTHER SHIP WOULD HAVE BEEN...

THE ACCELERATION HAD THROWN DAN AND THE OTHERS THE LENGTH OF THE CONTROL ROOM...

NOW THEY WILL HAVE TO PICK UP THE PITTAR BEFORE THEY FOLLOW US AND ATTACK!

IT WILL GIVE US PRECIOUS TIME!

DANDERR....

I WAS EXAMINING THE CONTROL SETTINGS! WE ARE MOVING ON A PREDICTED COURSE TO JUPITER— RIGHT INTO THE THICK OF THE PITTAR SHIPPING LINES!

DAN DARE in THE MENACE FROM JUPITER

It was a Pittar scoutship, blasted by Pittar missiles, and powerless! With Dan Dare, Digby and Bro the Veran on board, it plunged down into the poisonous atmosphere of Jupiter – heading towards certain destruction . . .

ON BOARD, DAN AND DIGBY WERE POWERLESS, IN THE STEADILY INCREASING AND COLOSSAL GRAVITATIONAL FIELD. BRO, THE LITTLE VERAN, WAS WRESTLING WITH THE GIANT CONTROLS...

YOU MIGHT AS WELL GIVE UP BRO — WE'VE HAD IT!

NO! THE RETRO-ROCKET ACTIVATOR SWITCH IS MOVING!

BUT WAS IT TOO LATE?

IMPACT!

WITH A SUDDEN BLAST OF ENERGY, THE RETRO-ROCKETS IN THE NOSE OF THE GIANT SCOUT-SHIP FLARED INTO LIFE...

A GRIM JARRING AND BOUNCING — AND THEN ALL WAS STILL! INSIDE THE SHIP THERE WAS A CHAOS OF WRECKAGE...

WELL, DIGBY, AT LEAST WE'VE COME THROUGH IT ALIVE!

UHH — THE GRAVITY-FIELD! I CAN HARDLY MOVE A LIMB....!

STAY WHERE YOU ARE — DO NOT EVEN TRY TO MOVE!

LITTLE BRO WAS MOVING AS EFFORTLESSLY THROUGH THE TITANIC G-FIELD AS A FISH THROUGH WATER...

WE HAVE COME DOWN SAFELY ON LAND! MY FEAR WAS THAT WE MIGHT LAND IN ONE OF THE ACID SEAS — IN WHICH CASE OUR FATE WOULD HAVE BEEN UNTHINKABLE...

I WILL NOW TRY TO BRING HELP!

BRO LEAPT FROM THE SMASHED HULL INTO A SCENE WHICH WAS AS HOMELY TO HIM AS IS A FOREST ON EARTH TO A HUNTER...

THERE IS BOUND TO BE A COLONY OF VERANS WITHIN REACH OF MY R.T.! SO HAVE COURAGE — AND BE PATIENT!

BUT INSIDE THE HULL, PRESSED DOWN BY THE CRUSHING FORCE...

THIS MAY BE ALL RIGHT FOR BRO — BUT IT'S LIKE TEN TONS OF BRICKS ON TOP OF ME! I DON'T THINK I'M GOING TO MAKE IT, DAN!

YOU'VE GOT TO, DIGBY! SHUT YOUR EYES — AND HOPE FOR THE BEST!

DAN DARE in THE MENACE FROM JUPITER

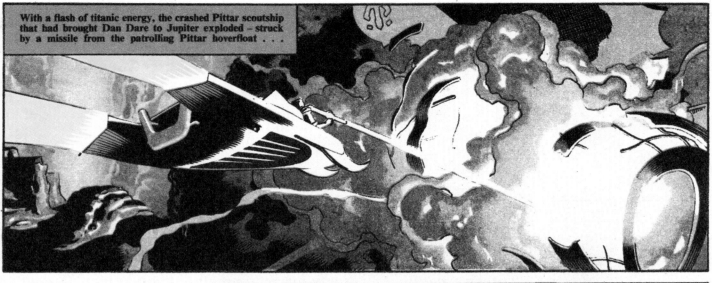

With a flash of titanic energy, the crashed Pittar scoutship that had brought Dan Dare to Jupiter exploded — struck by a missile from the patrolling Pittar hoverfloat . . .

IN UNDERGROWTH, A SAFE DISTANCE AWAY...

JUST AS YOU SAID, BRO — THESE MONSTERS SHOOT ON SIGHT!

STEPPING FROM THE HOVERFLOAT, THE PITTAR SUSPICIOUSLY SCANNED HIS SURROUNDINGS FOR SIGNS OF LIFE...

THAT IS HOW THEY OVER-RAN OUR PLANET, DANDERR — THEY TALK NO TERMS, MAKE NO PARLEYS!

HAVE YOU VERANS **NO WEAPON** WITH WHICH SUCH A MONSTER CAN BE ATTACKED?

ONLY ONE HAND-PROJECTILE, DANDERR — BUT IT IS USELESS *AGAINST THEIR BODY-ARMOUR!*

AND THIS IS THE PROJECTILE — DIGBY, DO YOU REMEMBER HOW WE BEAT THE PITTAR ON THE SHIP?

YOU OTHERS STAY UNDER COVER — THIS NEEDS ONLY ONE MAN, AND ONE SHOT!

A weird and fantastic battle was taking place on Jupiter – between Colonel Dan Dare and a giant Pittar invader!

DAN DARE
in THE MENACE FROM JUPITER

AND THAT, MY FRIENDS, IS HOW IT IS DONE! WE NOW KNOW THE SINGLE WEAKNESS IN THE PITTAR ARMOUR!

THE SINGLE PROJECTILE HAD FOUND ITS MARK! WITH VISOR SMASHED, THE GIANT HULK OF THE PITTAR MONSTER TOPPLED—

DIGBY, AND THE AMAZED VERANS, EMERGED FROM THE UNDERGROWTH...

DO ANY OF THE VERANS KNOW HOW THIS THING WORKS?

IT IS INCREDIBLE... DANDERR SLEW THE PITTAR SINGLE-HANDED...

LITTLE BRO TURNED TRIUMPHANTLY TO THE OTHER VERANS...

DO YOU STILL DOUBT, MY BROTHERS, THAT THE EARTHMEN ARE HERE TO HELP US?

TO TACKLE A PITTAR, SO—WE HAVE NOT SEEN SUCH COURAGE!

OH GREAT ONE—

OUR PROBLEM AT THE MOMENT, FRIENDS, IS TO MAKE THIS THING WORK! SO LET'S HAVE IDEAS, NOT TALK...

BUT IT WAS DIGBY WHO GOT THE CONTROLS GOING!

OKAY, COLONEL, THERE SHE BLOWS!

GOOD OLD DIGBY!

THE HOVERFLOAT MOVED SMOOTHLY ON ITS WAY...

GET US TO THE VERAN ENCAMPMENT, DIGBY!

SURE, COLONEL— BRO KNOWS THE WAY!

DAN TALKED WITH BRO—ABOUT OTHER THINGS!

THE TROUBLE WITH YOUR PEOPLE, BRO, IS THAT THEY ARE NOT RUTHLESS ENOUGH FOR WAR!

IT IS TRUE, DANDERR—THE PITTAR INVADERS DEMORALISED THEM! BUT WITH YOU TO LEAD US...

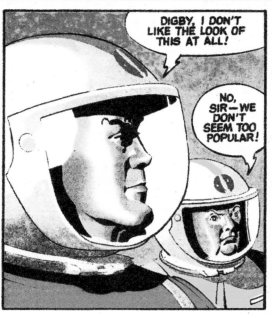

DAN DARE in **THE MENACE FROM JUPITER**

Although Dan and Digby were on Jupiter to help the Verans fight the giant Pittars, it was the Verans who captured Dan and Digby – to hand them over to the Pittars!

—YES, IF WE HAND THESE EARTHLINGS OVER TO THE MIGHTY ONES, WE MAY AT LAST BE LEFT IN PEACE!

A WISE IDEA!

ON THE HOVERFLOAT...

WE COME HERE TO HELP THESE CREATURES, AND THIS IS WHAT THEY DO TO US!

THEY'VE HAD TOO MUCH WAR, DIGBY—IT'S TURNED THEM INTO RABBITS!

LITTLE BRO, THE VERAN, WAS THROWN IN TO JOIN THEM...

YOU TOO WILL BE DELIVERED TO THE PITTARS!

DANDERR, I AM SORRY MY PEOPLE ARE SUCH FOOLS...

IT'S NOT YOUR FAULT, BRO—THERE WAS NOTHING ANY OF US COULD DO!

GATHERING VELOCITY, THE HOVERFLOAT BEGAN TO SCUD SWIFTLY ACROSS THE WEIRD TERRAIN...

AT ITS CONTROLS...

LET US NOW SEND AN R.T. MESSAGE TO THE PITTARS...

—YES, LET US TELL THEM WE BRING PRISONERS, AND COME IN PEACE!

AND NO ONE WAS WATCHING THE PRISONERS!

MY BODY SHIELDS YOU— ACT QUICKLY!

GOT THE BLASTER, DIGBY?

SURE THING, DAN!

A THIN JET OF FIRE QUICKLY VAPOURISED DAN'S BONDS...

IN AN INSTANT, DAN WAS FREEING THE OTHERS...

OUR ONLY HOPE OF ESCAPE IS OVER THE SIDE! COME ON!

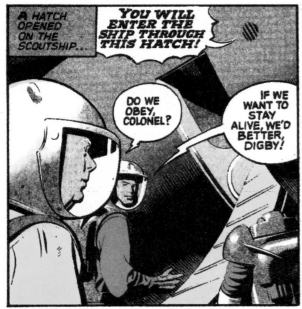

DAN DARE in **THE MENACE FROM JUPITER**

Colonel Dan Dare, Digby, and little Bro, the Veran, were prisoners in a chamber on a Pittar scoutship — and the walls of the chamber were so perfectly mirrored that they had a staggering illusion of standing in sheer space!

IT'S UNCANNY, SIR— YOU CAN HARDLY BELIEVE WE'RE STILL ON A SHIP!

A CLEVER DEVICE, DIGBY, FOR BAFFLING PRISONERS! ANYWAY, LET'S WAIT DEVELOPMENTS...

AND NOT FAR FROM THE PRISONERS...

AYE, THE LORD OF THE PITTARS WILL HAVE GOOD SPORT WITH THESE CREATURES!

HE IS ALWAYS INTERESTED IN NOVELTIES— AND TWO OF THEM ARE CLEARLY NOT FROM JUPITER!

RISING FROM THE JUPITER WILDERNESS, THE GIANT SCOUTSHIP ACCELERATED ACROSS THE FANTASTIC LANDSCAPE...

IN THE MIRROR-CHAMBER, AS TIME PASSED...

ENGINES STILL THUNDERING AFTER HALF AN HOUR — WHEREVER WE'RE GOING, IT'S QUITE A JOURNEY!

AND A SHIP LIKE THIS IS FOR ATMOSPHERE ONLY— SO WE HAVEN'T LEFT THE PLANET!

UNKNOWN TO THE EARTHMEN, THE PITTAR SCOUTSHIP WAS ARRIVING AT A GREAT METROPOLIS...

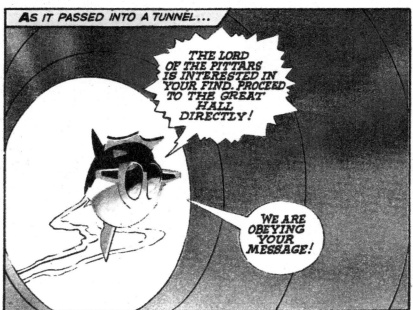

AS IT PASSED INTO A TUNNEL...

THE LORD OF THE PITTARS IS INTERESTED IN YOUR FIND. PROCEED TO THE GREAT HALL DIRECTLY!

WE ARE OBEYING YOUR MESSAGE!

AND IN THE MIRROR-CHAMBER INSIDE THE SHIP...

THEY'VE JUST SHUT OFF THE ENGINES, DIGBY...

LOOK, SIR— THE HATCH IS RE-OPENING!

THE PRISONERS WILL NOW LEAVE THIS SHIP!

LOOKS LIKE WE'RE SOMEWHERE IMPORTANT!

BUT WHERE? WHAT HAPPENS NOW?

DAN DARE

...in... THE MENACE FROM JUPITER

In a gigantic building in the heart of a Pittar metropolis on the planet Jupiter, Dan Dare, Digby and the Veran Bro had been brought before the Pittar overlord...

SO THESE ARE THE STRANGE PRISONERS?

WE BROUGHT THEM DIRECTLY TO YOU, LORD, OUT OF THE WILDERNESS. THEY WERE NEAR A COLONY OF VERANS WE HAD VAPORIZED...

AIEE—IT IS THE LORD OF THE PITTARS HIMSELF!

PULL YOURSELF TOGETHER, BRO— GET ON YOUR FEET! DON'T SHOW THESE CREATURES YOU'RE AFRAID...!

AND AS DAN HAULED BRO TO HIS FEET, HE REMEMBERED THE STRANGE BEHAVIOUR OF THE OTHER VERANS...

WE ARE HELPLESS, DANDERR! NO WEAPONS, NOTHING TO FIGHT WITH...

BUT FOR PETE'S SAKE, DON'T TELL THEM THAT! THERE'S AN OLD EARTH SAYING, AND A GOOD ONE—WHILE THERE'S LIFE, THERE'S HOPE!

YET BRO HAD GOOD CAUSE FOR FEAR! FOR AS THE LORD OF THE PITTARS SAW THAT ONE OF THE PRISONERS WAS A VERAN...

SO THERE IS A VERAN AMONG THEM? TAKE THEM ALL AWAY, AND DESTROY THEM!

WAIT, LORD...!

...YOU COULD HAVE SPORT WITH THEM BY PUTTING THEM TO THE ORDEAL...

...THEN WE WOULD NOT LOSE OUR REWARD FOR BRINGING THEM...

NOT WORTH THE TROUBLE! IF THEY MIX WITH VERANS, THEY ARE COWARDS!

AT THAT INSTANT...

O.K.—THEIR ATTENTION IS OFF US! LET'S TRY TO GET OUT OF HERE!

BUT AS COLONEL DARE HURLED HIMSELF SIDEWAYS...

UUUH?

IT'S SOME KIND OF PROTECTIVE FORCE-SCREEN!

HA—VERY AMUSING! SO THE CREATURES HAVE COURAGE AFTER ALL!

VERY WELL, LET US SET THEM AN ORDEAL. SINCE THEY HAVE COURAGE, WE WILL LET THEM DIE FIGHTING!

DAN DARE in THE MENACE FROM JUPITER

A strange scene in the *City of the Pittars* on Jupiter — with Little Bro spread-eagled on a platform in the middle of a small arena. As Colonel Dare stepped off the platform on which the Pittars had placed him, a weird machine rolled silently forward with terrifying speed...

IF WE CAN ONLY GET THAT BLASTER OVER THERE...

LOOK OUT, SIR!

WITH SWIFT REFLEXES, DAN LEAPT FOR THE SAFETY OF THE PLATFORM...

...AND THE MACHINE INSTANTLY WHIRLED ROUND IN ITS TRACKS, AND RETURNED TO ITS GUARD OVER THE BLASTER...

GET THE POINT, DIGBY? AS LONG AS WE STAY PUT, SO DOES THE MACHINE! BUT I THINK I KNOW HOW TO FOX IT! IF WE BOTH LEAP OFF AT THE SAME TIME, AND ON OPPOSITE SIDES OF THE ARENA...

O.K., SIR — I GET IT!

A FEW MOMENTS LATER, THE PLAN WAS PUT INTO ACTION...

NOW!

ROGER!

THE MACHINE SAT WHIRRING UNCERTAINLY...

DON'T WORRY, BRO— WE'LL GET YOU OUT OF HERE!

I HOPE SO...

AT DIGBY'S SHOUT, THE MACHINE MOVED— TOWARDS DIGBY...

NOW'S YOUR CHANCE, SIR!

SWIFTLY, DAN DIVED FOR THE BLASTER...

GOT IT!

BUT WAS A SINGLE BLASTER OF ANY USE AGAINST A HURTLING DEADLY MECHANISM?

DAN DARE in THE MENACE FROM JUPITER

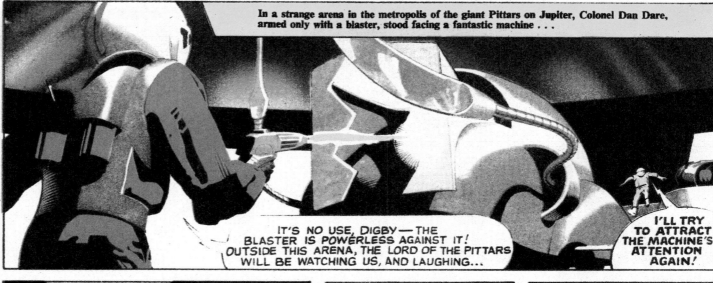

In a strange arena in the metropolis of the giant Pittars on Jupiter, Colonel Dan Dare, armed only with a blaster, stood facing a fantastic machine . . .

IT'S NO USE, DIGBY—THE BLASTER IS POWERLESS AGAINST IT! OUTSIDE THIS ARENA, THE LORD OF THE PITTARS WILL BE WATCHING US, AND LAUGHING...

I'LL TRY TO ATTRACT THE MACHINE'S ATTENTION AGAIN!

BUT THE LORD OF THE PITTARS WAS NOT LAUGHING. AT THAT VERY MOMENT, NEAR THE ARENA...

AAAGH—GHAAGH!

HE MAKES A STRANGE SOUND!

THE HIGH LORD STAGGERS

HE IS ILL!

AND IN THE ARENA ITSELF, A STRANGE HAPPENING!

THE MACHINE HAS GONE DEAD, DIGBY! IT'S AS THOUGH SOME KIND OF CONTROL HAS BEEN REMOVED!

MAYBE IT'S ANOTHER PITTAR TRICK...

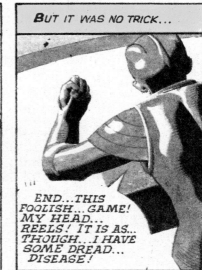

BUT IT WAS NO TRICK...

END...THIS FOOLISH...GAME! MY HEAD... REELS! IT IS AS... THOUGH...I HAVE SOME DREAD... DISEASE!

AND THE PITTAR LORD, EMITTING SNARLING, SNEEZING SOUNDS, CAREERED WILDLY DOWN THE GREAT HALL!

AAAGH—GHAAGH!

HE HAS GONE MAD!

YET WE CANNOT TOUCH HIM— HE IS THE SUPREME LORD!

AT THE SMALL ARENA, THE FORCE SCREEN SURROUNDING IT HAD GONE!

SOMETHING HAS HAPPENED!

AT LEAST WE'VE NOW GOT THE BLASTER! SO LET'S FREE BRO WHILE WE HAVE THE CHANCE!

I AM GRATEFUL TO YOU...

COLONEL DAN, DIGBY, AND THE LITTLE VERAN MOVED CAUTIOUSLY OUT INTO A DESERTED HALL!

THE PLACE LOOKS AS THOUGH A CYCLONE HAS STRUCK IT!

NOT FAR AWAY, IN A VAST CONTROL ROOM, A BERSERK AND REELING LORD OF THE PITTARS WAS SMASHING BLINDLY AROUND HIM!

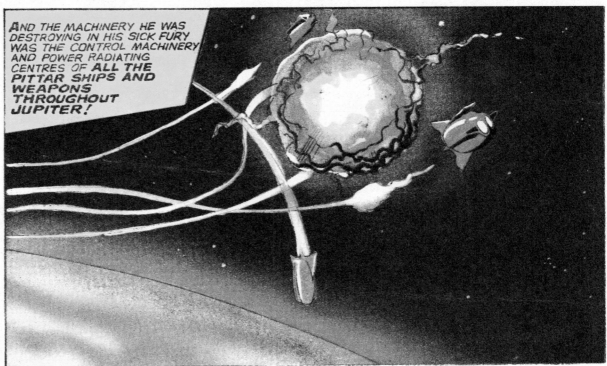

AND THE MACHINERY HE WAS DESTROYING IN HIS SICK FURY WAS THE CONTROL MACHINERY AND POWER RADIATING CENTRES OF ALL THE PITTAR SHIPS AND WEAPONS THROUGHOUT JUPITER!

DAN DARE THE **MENACE FROM JUPITER**

On Jupiter, Dan Dare, Digby and Bro, the little Veran, were trapped in the hall of the Pittars, the race of giants who had invaded the planet. Suddenly, the Lord High Pittar went berserk, smashing controls and machinery which affected the radiating centres of the Pittar stronghold . . .

HE IS CRAZED! HE WILL SMASH EVERYTHING IN SIGHT! ALL OUR CONTROLS...

WE MUST STOP HIM BEFORE HE KILLS US ALL!

I MUST DO WHAT I MUST DO.

AAAH!

DAN DARE, DIGBY AND BRO STARED AT THE SCENE IN UTTER AMAZEMENT...

I HAVE NEVER SEEN THE PITTARS BEHAVE LIKE THIS BEFORE. THEY ARE WITHOUT PITY— BUT THEY DO NOT KILL EACH OTHER!

THEY CAN KILL AS MANY AS THEY LIKE— THE MORE THE BETTER!

SUDDENLY...

AAA-CHOO-OOO!

MY THROAT— IT IS ON FIRE! I CANNOT BREATHE...

LET'S GET OUT OF HERE WHILE WE CAN. THEY'VE GOT TOO MANY TROUBLES OF THEIR OWN TO WORRY ABOUT US.

IF WE CAN REACH THE OUTSIDE, WE'LL BE SAFE.

BUT BRO DISCOVERED THAT DIGBY HAD SPOKEN TOO SOON...

THEY ARE COMING AFTER US, DANDERR!

THERE'S NOT AN INCH OF COVER. WE'VE HAD IT THIS TIME, SIR!

THEY'VE IGNORED US! THEY'RE RUNNING AWAY!

THEY MAKE FOR THE SPACE-FLEET CENTRE!

ATISHOO!

SUDDENLY, DAN BURST INTO LAUGHTER...

WELL, I'LL BE...! I'VE JUST REALIZED WHAT'S HAPPENING!

DAN DARE

in THE MENACE FROM JUPITER

On the planet Jupiter, the invading giant Pittars went berserk, smashing controls and machinery. Suddenly, they dashed from their stronghold and made for the space fleet centre, watched by Dan Dare, Digby and little Bro . . .

I'VE JUST REALIZED WHAT'S HAPPENED! DON'T YOU SEE—THEY'VE CAUGHT COLD!

EEH! I MAY BE DAFT, BUT WHY SHOULD A COLD MAKE THEM RUN AWAY?

THEY'VE NEVER ENCOUNTERED COLD GERMS BEFORE. OUR BODIES ARE USED TO THEM, SO WE MERELY GET A RUNNY NOSE AND A TEMPERATURE...

...BUT TO THE PITTARS, A COLD IS MORE DEADLY THAN BUBONIC PLAGUE...!

THEIR HIGHLY-DEVELOPED INTELLIGENCE TELLS THEM THEY CANNOT FIGHT THIS DISEASE—SO THEY ARE EVACUATING!

O MIGHTY DANDERR, I HAD BUT LITTLE HOPE OF HELP WHEN I CAME TO YOUR EARTH. BUT YOU HAVE SAVED MY PEOPLE.

DON'T THANK ME, BRO. YOU MUST THANK DIGBY—AND THAT SNIFFLE HE'S HAD EVER SINCE WE LEFT HOME!

Although the Earth fleet had withdrawn millions of miles away on Dan's instructions, Digby set to work to build a radio transmitter from the wrecked Pittar machinery. It seemed a hopeless task, but he managed it – and, to everyone's amazement, contacted the fleet. One of the ships headed towards Jupiter and, before long . . .

COLONEL DARE, WE'VE BEEN WORRIED STIFF ABOUT YOU. IN FACT, WE ONLY RECEIVED YOUR MESSAGE BECAUSE WE HAD DECIDED TO FIND YOU AT ALL COSTS.

ALL'S WELL NOW, THANKS TO MY OLD FRIEND DIGBY.

JUPITER BELONGS TO YOU AGAIN, BRO—TO YOU AND THE VERANS. REBUILD IT AND LIVE IN PEACE. WHO KNOWS, ONE DAY I MAY RETURN—BUT THE PITTARS WILL NEVER RETURN!

FAREWELL, LORD HIGH DANDERR.

THREE CHEERS FOR LORD HIGH DANDERR...

WELL, DIGBY, THAT'S THE END OF THAT. I WONDER WHAT WE'LL FIND WAITING FOR US WHEN WE GET HOME!

WHATEVER IT IS, COLONEL DAN, YOU CAN BET IT'LL BE SOMETHING EXCITING— ATISHOO!

DAN DARE

AND as their spaceship hurtled towards Earth, another of Dan Dare's adventures came to an end. What was waiting for them on their return? They did not know. But Digby was right when he said it would be something exciting.

A fortnight after they had landed, Dan was sent for by the Prime Minister – and appointed CONTROLLER OF THE SPACEFLEET. And a week later at a presentation ceremony attended by former companions who had shared many of his perilous space adventures, Dan was warmly congratulated by his ex-chief, Sir Hubert Guest . . .

THE incredible adventures of Dan Dare have made his name famous throughout the world – indeed throughout the Universe. Seldom can one man have packed so much excitement into so short a time. But as he gets to grips with his new job, his adventures must come to a temporary halt.

One of the tasks which will keep him deskbound is the request by World Space Control that he should put on record the story of his amazing career. It is intended that the completed manual shall be presented to every Space Cadet as he begins his training.

We, too, have been looking back at some of his exploits, and we have decided to give *today's* Space Cadets a preview of the manual's contents.

Beginning next week, we shall be recalling some of Dan's greatest adventures. It's a series you can't afford to miss!

SPECIAL BONUS!
DAN DARE
8 PAGE ADVENTURE
REPRINTED FROM THE
EAGLE
ANNUAL
NUMBER EIGHT

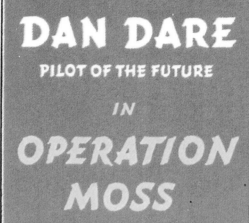

DAN DARE
PILOT OF THE FUTURE
IN
OPERATION MOSS

GOOD MORNING, CHIEF! WHERE DO I GO *THIS* TIME?

ON A BOFFIN RUN TO "Q.3".

Q.3? THAT'S THE NEW PLANET IN OLD CHARLIE BUNN'S SOOT-BAG, ISN'T IT?

"COAL-SACK", DAN — NOT "SOOT-BAG"! IF YOUR PASSENGER HEARS THAT SERVICE SLANG, YOU'LL GET A PROPER ROCKET!

HE CERTAINLY WILL!

PROFESSOR JOCELYN PEABODY! MY FAVOURITE BOFFIN!

I PREFER TO BE CALLED A *SCIENTIST*, COLONEL DARE!

... AND FOR YOUR INFORMATION, DOCTOR CHARLES BUNN IS ONE OF OUR MOST EMINENT BRAINS. FURTHER, THE TERM "COALSACK" MEANS...

I KNOW, PROF! I WAS ONLY FOOLING.

A "COALSACK" IS A DARK PATCH IN THE FIRMAMENT, PARTICULARLY MARKED NEAR THE *SOUTHERN CROSS* IN THE *MILKY WAY*, WHICH IS A LUMINOUS BAND OF COUNTLESS STARS SITUATED —

YOUR SCIENTIFIC TERMS ARE A BIT OUT-OF-DATE IN VIEW OF RECENT COSMIC RESEARCH, COLONEL!

HOLD IT, YOU TWO! YOU'LL HAVE PLENTY OF TIME TO ARGUE ON THE WAY TO "Q.3".

PAX, PROFESSOR?

PEACE, PILOT!

THERE'S YOUR DESTINATION, DAN!

THAT'S NEW SKY TO ME! THERE'S A PARTY OF SCIENTISTS OUT THERE ALREADY, I BELIEVE?

YES, LED BY DOCTOR BUNN. THEY'VE BEEN EXPLORING "Q.3" FOR THREE MONTHS.

HERE'S YOUR PRE-PLOTTED COURSE, DAN. FEED THIS INTO THE NEW ELECTROPILOT.

THERE'S NOTHING LEFT FOR FLESH-AND-BLOOD PILOTS TO DO THESE DAYS BUT LEAVE IT TO "GEORGE" — THE OLD ELECTROBOT!

YOU'LL TAKE PROFESSOR PEABODY TO "Q.3", PICK UP THE STUFF THE SCIENTISTS HAVE DUG UP AND RETURN TO BASE.

THE MATERIAL FOUND BY MY FELLOW SCIENTISTS MAY BE OF INESTIMABLE VALUE — TO SCIENTIFIC PROGRESS.

WELL, PROFESSOR PEABODY, YOU'RE IN SAFE HANDS. DAN'S THE BEST PILOT THERE IS!

AT THE LAUNCHING RAMP...

PROF PEABODY SCARES ME TO DEATH, SIR! CHATTING WITH HER IS LIKE GOING BACK TO ASTRAL COLLEGE FOR A REFRESHER COURSE!

DON'T WORRY, DIG! SHE'S GOT A HEART OF PURE GOLD —

FRANK HAMPSON & DON HARLEY.

— AND A HEAD OF PURE SCIENCE!

TAKE-OFF

5-4-3-2-1-ZERO!

TEN DAYS LATER...

"Q.3'S" IN VISION PROFESSOR! COME AND TAKE A LOOK AT THIS "NEW-OLD" PLANET OF YOURS.

THERE SHE IS!

DIAMETER APPROXIMATELY—

KEEP IT SIMPLE FOR DIGBY. SAY IT'S ABOUT THE SAME SIZE AS THE EARTH!

JUST WHAT DO YOU KNOW ABOUT "Q.3"?

GRAVITY ALMOST IDENTICAL WITH EARTH'S...ATMOSPHERE REQUIRES ONLY .07 ADJUSTMENT ON SPACE-SUIT BREATHING APPARATUS...TEMPERATURE OVER THE PERIOD OF INVESTIGATION IS 40.9.

THERE SEEMS TO BE NO FORM OF ANIMAL OR VEGETABLE LIFE OTHER THAN A PECULIAR MOSS-LIKE GROWTH THAT CARPETS MOST OF THE EXPLORED AREA.

NO SIGN OF PREVIOUS CIVILISATION?

THAT'S WHY I'M HERE. THE ARCHAEOLOGISTS THOUGHT A BOTANIST MIGHT HELP THEM TO DECIPHER SOMETHING THEY'VE FOUND...

WHATEVER HAS BOTANY GOT TO DO WITH INSCRIPTIONS ON DESERTED PLANETS?

AH, YOU WAIT AND SEE!

SPACE DRIVE OUT! G. MINUS 500! CHANGE OVER FROM AUTO TO MANUAL CONTROL... G. MINUS 400...300...

WELCOME TO "Q.3".

THANK YOU, DOCTOR BUNN... YOU KNOW COLONEL DARE OF SPACEFLEET?

WHO DOESN'T? YOU'LL FIND YOUR VISIT VERY INTERESTING, COLONEL.

I'M SURE I WILL, SIR!

BEYOND DOUBT THIS PLANET WAS POPULATED BY A HIGHLY INTELLIGENT RACE.

WHAT BECAME OF THEM, SIR?

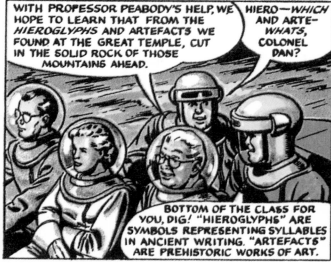

WITH PROFESSOR PEABODY'S HELP, WE HOPE TO LEARN THAT FROM THE HIEROGLYPHS AND ARTEFACTS WE FOUND AT THE GREAT TEMPLE, CUT IN THE SOLID ROCK OF THOSE MOUNTAINS AHEAD.

HIERO—WHICH AND ARTE-WHATS, COLONEL DAN?

BOTTOM OF THE CLASS FOR YOU, DIG! "HIEROGLYPHS" ARE SYMBOLS REPRESENTING SYLLABLES IN ANCIENT WRITING. "ARTEFACTS" ARE PREHISTORIC WORKS OF ART.

WHATEVER THEY LOOKED LIKE, THE LATE INHABITANTS OF Q.3. CERTAINLY KNEW HOW TO BUILD.

THE "WRITING PICTURES" ON THE TEMPLE WALLS SHOW THE INHABITANTS WERE CLOSELY SIMILAR TO EARTHMEN — THOUGH I SUSPECT THEY REACHED THEIR PEAK OF CIVILISATION MANY CENTURIES AGO.

WHAT'S THIS DOCTOR?

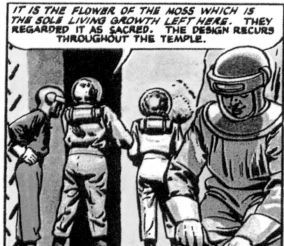

IT IS THE FLOWER OF THE MOSS WHICH IS THE SOLE LIVING GROWTH LEFT HERE. THEY REGARDED IT AS SACRED. THE DESIGN RECURS THROUGHOUT THE TEMPLE.

I'LL TAKE A BIT BACK AS A SOUVENIR.

OLD DIGBY'S QUARTERS ARE CLUTTERED UP WITH SOUVENIRS OF ALL THE PLANETS HE'S VISITED!

BUT, AS THINGS TURN OUT, DIGBY'S COLLECTING HABIT SAVES EARTH FROM THE SAME CATASTROPHE WHICH, AEONS BEFORE, DESTROYED CIVILISATION ON PLANET "Q.3."

IN THE MAIN HALL OF THE TEMPLE.

BEHOLD, — THE GREAT TEMPLE OF "Q.3."

FANTASTIC!

HOW DID YOU FIX THIS LIGHTING, DR BUNN?

IT IS SOME KIND OF LUMINOUS QUARTZ, HITHERTO UNKNOWN, AND STILL ACTIVE AFTER TIME IMMEMORIAL.

THOSE "Q3" DWELLERS WERE RIGHT SMART LADS!

THIS FLOWER SEEMS TO BE THE CENTRAL SYMBOL OF THE TEMPLE.

WHAT'S IN THE URN?

IT CONTAINS NOTHING BUT HARD, SHRIVELLED PELLETS — RATHER LIKE SEEDS OF SOME TYPE...

WE WANT YOU TO TAKE BACK THIS URN AND ALSO THE STONE UPON WHICH IT RESTS. YOU WILL PASS THEM OVER TO THE CURATOR OF THE BRITISH MUSEUM.

STRANGE HOW OFTEN THE "MOSS FLOWER" APPEARS.

THAT'S WHY WE THOUGHT PROFESSOR PEABODY'S BOTANICAL KNOWLEDGE WOULD HELP THE DECODING.

IN A WEEK OR SO PERHAPS WE'LL GIVE YOU THE ANSWER!

I WONDER WHAT THAT MEANS...? IT LOOKS AS IF...

RATHER HER THAN ME!

COME ON, DIG! LET'S LEAVE HER TO IT!

NEXT DAY

THE ALTAR-STONE IS IN THAT CRATE, COLONEL, BUT I THINK YOU'D BETTER STORE THIS URN IN THE CODE-CABINET, ALONG WITH YOUR SHIP'S PAPERS.

THE OLD "CRASH-LOCKER", EH?

DON'T SAY IT, COLONEL DAN!

DIGBY!... WHAT'S IN YOUR BOX?

MY SOUVENIR — A SPECIMEN OF "Q.3" MOSS.

CHEERIO, PROF! HOPE YOU MANAGE TO WORK IT OUT!

AND I HOPE YOU MAKE A HAPPY EARTHFALL, COLONEL!

DAN AND DIGBY BEGIN THE LONG RETURN JOURNEY TO EARTH, LITTLE KNOWING THAT THEY ARE CARRYING A PERIL AS GREAT AS A COBALT BOMB.

GOOD OLD EARTH!

IT'S NICE TO BE HOME AGAIN!

SAFEST PLACE ANYWHERE, COLONEL DAN. WE'VE GOT COMPLETE DEFENCE AGAINST ANYTHING FROM OUTER SPACE NOWADAYS.

WHAT'S IT LIKE ON "Q.3." DAN?

THERE'S PLENTY OF EVIDENCE THAT IT WAS ONCE POPULATED BY A RACE SIMILAR TO OUR OWN, SIR.

FORGIVE ME FOR NOT SALUTING, SIR — BUT I'VE GOT MY ARMS FULL OF "HIEROFACTS" AND "ARTEGLYPHS" AND A BIT OF "Q.3." MOSS I'M GOING TO TRY AND GROW IN A POT!

WATCH YOUR STEP, DIG!

OH, CRUMBS!

WELL C-CAUGHT, SIR!

DEAD LUCKY! IF THIS PIECE OF "Q.3." POTTERY HAD GOT BROKEN, WE'D NEVER HAVE HEARD THE LAST OF IT FROM PROFESSOR PEABODY!

WHAT IS IT?

NOBODY KNOWS YET, SIR! IT'S GOT TO GO TO THE BRITISH MUSEUM UNTIL PROFESSOR PEABODY RETURNS AND VETS IT.

DON'T MISS ANY DIG!

NOT LIKELY, SIR!

THAT'S THE LOT, SIR!

NO HARM DONE, THANK GOODNESS!

BUT, AS THE SPACEMEN MOVE ON, ONE SMALL PELLET IS LEFT —

A TINY SEED WHICH IS TO GROW A HARVEST OF TERROR.

AS DAN'S HELIJET CIRCLES "BLUE FIELD", SIR HUBERT GIVES EARTH'S TOP SPACE ACE THE "GEN".

IT'S LIKE A FUNGUS. WE'VE HAD NO CHANCE TO GET A FULL-GROWN SPECIMEN BECAUSE THEY SIMPLY BLEW UP IN THE FACES OF THE VOLUNTEERS WHO WENT OUT TO COLLECT THEM.

AND REPORTS ARE COMING IN OF THEM SPRINGING UP ELSEWHERE.

WE'VE SENT BULLDOZERS, FLAME-THROWERS, PLANT-KILLER SPRAY PLANES, AND THE LOT TO TRY AND STOP THEM, BUT THEY SIMPLY OVER-WHELMED EVERYTHING.

AS DAN SWOOPS LOW OVER "BLUE FIELD" A SCENE OF DEVASTATION MEETS HIS STARTLED EYES.

GREAT GRIEF! WHERE DID THE FILTHY THING COME FROM?

IT STARTED CLOSE TO YOUR SHIP. COULD YOU HAVE BROUGHT IT BACK FROM "Q.3"?

IMPOSSIBLE! DOCTOR BUNN'S PARTY SAID THERE IS NO FAUNA OR FLORA THERE, EXCEPT THAT QUEER LOOKING MOSS.

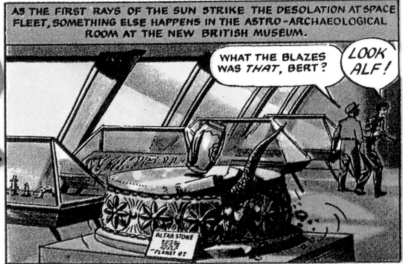

AS THE FIRST RAYS OF THE SUN STRIKE THE DESOLATION AT SPACE FLEET, SOMETHING ELSE HAPPENS IN THE ASTRO-ARCHAEOLOGICAL ROOM AT THE NEW BRITISH MUSEUM.

WHAT THE BLAZES WAS THAT, BERT?

LOOK ALF!

ALTAR STONE

HEL-LP!

I'M SEEING THINGS!

THAT AFTERNOON

EVENING PILOT

TWIN TERRORS STRIKE AT LONDON'S HEART

AS THE TWO ATTENDANTS RUSH TO REPORT THIS NEW DISASTER, THE STRANGE STARFISH-LIKE CREATURE, LED BY AN AGE-OLD INSTINCT, MAKES FOR ITS NATURAL FOOD.

HERE IT COMES AND IT'S GROWING BIGGER!

AND THERE'S MORE BEHIND— DOZENS!

By EVENING PILOT REPORTER

At nightfall yesterday, Spacefleet H.Q. was attacked by a strange growth. Scientists say that if it continues to reproduce at the rate already maintained, all England will be com-pletely covered *within five weeks!* Following in the wake of the deadly growth came monsters which feed on the pulp of these giant puffballs. These monsters rapidly in-crease in number by shedding a tentacle which immediately grows into another monster.

AS THE SHADOWS LENGTHEN OVER LONDON, EARTH CABINET MEETS TO DISCUSS THE EMERGENCY.

WE KNOW THREE THINGS — THIS VILE FUNGI GROWS ONLY AT NIGHT—THE STARFISH MONSTERS FEED BY DAY—AND MOST IMPORTANT, THOSE BEASTS CAME FROM PLANET "Q.3." IN THE ALTAR STONE BROUGHT BACK BY COLONEL DARE.

TWO FACTS ARE OBVIOUS — THE MONSTERS EXIST ON THE FUNGI. THE MULTIPLIED RATE OF BOTH IS SUCH THAT IF WE CAN FIND NO REMEDY THE WHOLE WORLD WILL BE OVER-RUN BY THESE PLAGUES IN LESS THAN A YEAR!

COLONEL DARE FLEW OVER THE "BLUE-FIELD" EARLIER TODAY. I WOULD LIKE YOU TO SEE THE FILM HE TOOK.

THE "Q.3." MOSS EXPLODES INTO INSTANT LIFE, DEVOURING THE WHITE PLAGUE FASTER THAN IT CAN GROW!

JUMPIN' JUPITER! THAT THERE MOSS IS FAIRLY *EATING UP* THOSE PUFFBALLS!

SO MY HUNCH *WAS* RIGHT!

DAWN! ALL GROWTH HAS CEASED AND PATROLS ARE MOPPING UP THE LAST OF THOSE MONSTROUS STARFISH.

IT'S A MIRACLE!

A MIRACLE OF OLD MOTHER NATURE'S!

WHAT MADE YOU THINK THAT MOSS WOULD DO THE TRICK, DARE?

WE BROUGHT THE SEED OF THOSE PUFFBALLS AND THE ALTAR-STONE CONTAINING THE FIRST OF THOSE STARFISH BACK FROM "Q.3."

GRANTED, BUT...

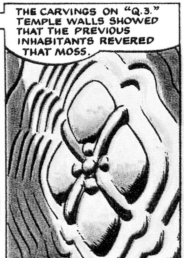

THE CARVINGS ON "Q.3." TEMPLE WALLS SHOWED THAT THE PREVIOUS INHABITANTS REVERED THAT MOSS.

SO YOU REALIZED THAT, AS THERE WAS NO GROWTH ON "Q.3." OTHER THAN THE MOSS...

...SOMETIME IN THE DIM PAST THE "Q.3." RACE HAD DISCOVERED IT WAS THE ANTIDOTE TO THE PUFFBALL PLAGUE.

SINCE THAT MOSS HAS WIPED OUT THE PUFFBALLS IT SEEMS TO HAVE STOPPED GROWING, BUT IT'S STILL GREEN AND LIVING.

PHEW! TO THINK ALL THAT CAME FROM MY LITTLE POT PLANT.

I HOPE WE WON'T FIND WE EXCHANGED A WHITE PLAGUE FOR A GREEN ONE!

BLUE FIELD — 3 WEEKS LATER.

WE FINALLY BROKE THE CODE ON THE "Q.3." LANGUAGE, COLONEL.

STILL, IT'S JUST AS WELL WE DIDN'T HAVE TO WAIT FOR YOUR ANSWER.

THANK GOODNESS YOU GUESSED RIGHT. THE WRITING ON THOSE TEMPLE WALLS TAUGHT US HOW THE SPORES OF THE PUFFBALLS WERE ACCIDENTALLY CARRIED FROM A REMOTE ISLAND TO THE MAINLAND OF "Q.3". CONDITIONS WERE PERFECT AND THEY GREW APACE.. THEY PROVED AN IDEAL FOOD FOR THE NATIVE STARFISH WHICH GREW TO GIGANTIC PROPORTIONS ON THIS NEW DIET. "Q.3" SCIENTISTS SOUGHT THE ANSWER AND EVENTUALLY FOUND IT IN THE MOSS. UP TILL THEN IT HAD ONLY GROWN IN ONE SMALL LOCALITY. THEY CALLED IT THE "MASTER MOSS" AND MADE IT A SACRED SYMBOL IN THEIR ANCIENT BELIEFS.

YOU CAN TELL THE REST OVER LUNCH, PROFESSOR. DIGBY IS PREPARING A SURPRISE DISH FOR YOU.

DAN'S QUARTERS.

GRUB UP! TODAY'S SPECIAL — "Q.3." SALAD!

WHILE YOU'VE BEEN "DECODING", YOUR FELLOW SCIENTISTS HAVE DISCOVERED THAT THIS MOSS MAKES A PERFECT FOOD.

WHAT ON EARTH...

— CONTAINING ALL THE NECESSARY CARBOHYDRATES, MINERAL SALTS, VITAMINS AND WHAT-HAVE-YOU.

WHAT'S MORE, IT WILL GROW ALMOST ANYWHERE AND IT'S EASY TO CONTROL.

MM, DELICIOUS.

IT'S GOING TO SOLVE A GOOD MANY OF THE FOOD PROBLEMS OF INTERPLANETARY TRAVEL AND EXPLORATION.

ALL THANKS TO DIGBY, THE ROLLING STONE THAT *DID* GATHER SOME MOSS!

AND A LUCKY THING I *DID!*

FRANK HAMPSON PRODUCTION.